Chronicles of a Gay Boy: X

By: Glend Martinez

Glend Martinez

GlendMartinez@BeGoodDoGoodPublications.com

Book Cover by Hallie Halpern

Senior Editor: Dashawn Hayes

Junior Editor: Diana Pardo De Armas

1st edition 2022

To Annie, Mirtha, Lourdes and Pete:

I am the man I am today because of you four.

Thank you for saving my life and gifting me the opportunity to succeed. Thank you for inviting me into your family and treating me as one of your own.

Thank you for never giving up on me.

I hope I make you proud.

I love you.

Chapter 1

Monday is my favorite day of the week. It's the beginning of a new week which means it's a new opportunity to succeed. I can't help but be overflowing with joy. It's my average Monday, my mom is taking me to school and she's treating me to a favorite breakfast, a Vanilla Frappuccino. Her and I have such an amazing bond that sometimes it feels like it's a relationship right out of a fairytale. She's a lawyer, so she's constantly telling me about her cases and how my dad gets tired of listening to her. I could never get tired of listening to her. I love our car rides to school but I especially love our Monday car rides. Monday is the start of a new week for my mom, and she's always fired up and ready to conquer the world. "Glend, what time do you get out today?!" My mom asks as she drives me to school. "Well, today's Monday so I have to help tutor a few kids and then I have swimming practice, so I'll probably be done around 5 but I spoke to Alex and his mom will take me to swimming practice and then home." I say as we approach my high school.

"I don't really like the idea of someone else taking you home, I'll call Alex's mom and see if she'll let me take you and Alex home." She says with a concerned tone. "Alright mom, it doesn't matter. I'll be fine with Alex's mom but whatever makes you feel more at ease." I say as I try to ease her worry. She's a lawyer working a million hours a week but somehow, she always finds the time to do the little things for me. "Alright then, remember I love you more than anyone.

You're always my number 1. Always just me and you." She says as she turns into school. "I love you too mommy, always just me and you." And in that moment, I woke up. Monday mornings are always spent wishing my life was as perfect as I dreamt it. A successful, happy, and concerned mom taking her son to school. If only that was really my life. I look for my phone and see that it's 6:00 am. Fuck, I only slept three hours last night.

Releasing a sigh of disappoint, I know I'll have to get up soon. I tried tossing and turning on this lumpy couch, but there is no chance of being able to go back to sleep. I stare at the ceiling and take one final pause before I say my prayer. "Hey God, it's me again. We made it through another weekend. It's finally Monday. Please God, let my mom be okay. Thank you for everything. Amen." I have to say it every Monday morning to get ready to start another week.

I put on my glasses and clearly see the small trailer I live in. No big mansion, no fancy closet, just my regular views. The trailer I live in is a duplex, the half I live in has one room, a living room and a kitchen. My mom and step dad stay in the room while I'm on the lumpy couch. I fold my covers and try to make the couch as presentable as possible. Not like it matters, it's not like either of them are even going to come out here.

They got back at ten last night and they didn't stop fighting until two in the morning. My stepdad works in construction and his only days off are Sunday and Monday. Since he "maintains" us, he feels like he can just do whatever he wants. He drinks like a sailor and mainly treats my mom and I like garbage. Some days he's tolerable and other days he's a drunk angry maniac.

I try to stay out of his sight when he's drunk to avoid any issues. I don't know what my mom sees in him. I make my way into the bedroom room and see that they're both in their usual drunk slumber. I approach her and put my hand on her chest to check if she's breathing and she is. "Thank you." I whisper to God. I'm seventeen years old, I haven't taken any CPR classes so, I guess this will have to do. I suddenly feel an overpowering sense of relief. Well, time to get ready for school. The bedroom has all of our clothes and the only bathroom. Since our space is so small, my stepdad says I can't have any drawers, so all my clothes are in trash bags. I used to organize my uniform the night before, but ever so often, my stepdad would came home in a drunken rage and throw it all away, along with my bookbag. After a handful of drunk episodes, I learned it's better to just keep my clothes in the room. Luckily, I have a trash bag system that helps me find all my clothes very easily. Life taught me to adapt and stay prepared so that's what I do. I find my uniform and quickly go in the bathroom. The bathroom is so small that literally only one person can be in it at a time.

The only good thing about this trailer is that it never runs out of hot water. I jump in the shower as quickly as I can. Washing my face, I think of what it would really be like to have your mom take you to school in the morning. My mom hasn't taken me to school since elementary, I don't even think she's ever stepped foot in my middle school, and she only went to my high school once to register my transfer. It really bothers me that she doesn't care but I still go because I want a way out of this poor way of living. I never tell her anything or complain but it would be nice if she made an effort to be involved or show interest. As the water falls on me, I feel a sense of peace. I love showering so much because it's when I do my best thinking. I can solve any problem in the shower. It's my fun little space away from all the negativity of my home life. I turn the water off, dry myself, brush my teeth and finish getting ready for school. It's extremely humid in the small trailer bathroom, but I try to get everything done as fast as possible so that I don't have to come in and out. I step out of the bathroom and walk back to my couch. I pick up my bookbag and make sure I have my essentials: twenty dollars, my headphones, and my homework. I take my phone off the charger to check the time and make sure the bus hasn't passed yet but I'm still early. I walk back into my mom's room, give her a kiss on the forehead and say, "I love you more than anyone.

You're always my number 1. Always just me and you." I love my dream life but it's all made up. My life is nothing like that and I know it. My mom might not be some powerful lawyer but she's still my mom and I will always love her. It'll always be just me and her. That part of the dream is never made up. I lock the door and rush to the bus stop. I'm not late but I would rather be safe than sorry. Luckily, the bus stop is right in front of my complex entrance. I'm 15 minutes earlier than scheduled and I still find the need to rush. I'm always there to catch the bus but sometimes it gets to the stop way earlier than expected. I always plan because one can never be too sure. Even though I'm rushing to the entrance, I still find time to admire all the cute trailers.

I'm not really picky when it comes to houses, but ideally, I want a two-story house; something nice, with a big lawn and a pool

for family days. Honestly, I would love any home as long as it's for me and my mom. I'm almost at the front but it's time to pass by my favorite trailer, I call it the Perfect Home or PH for short. PH is in between my current trailer and the entrance.
It has two entrances and, since it's in the corner, it has a really big backyard. It was just remodeled but the family decided to sell it and move. I've done my research on the trailer, sometimes I pose as a potential buyer and bombard the realtor with questions. Sometimes I think about dropping out and working full time to buy PH, but I know my mom wouldn't be happy. I'm sure buying property like that takes a lot of resources that I don't have. Plus, I wouldn't want my douchey stepdad to come, and she honestly can't live without him. I'll have my perfect home one day but until then it's the waiting game.

I reach the bus stop and see that there are other students there so the bus hasn't arrived. I will have eight hours of freedom before I have return to this hell. I look at my phone and it's 6:40 am so the bus will probably get here in the next five minutes. I know everyone at this bus stop goes to my school, but I don't really talk to any of them. I know I should, but I'd get embarrassed if they ask to come to my trailer, so I'd rather just avoid the situation. My close friends know my home isn't happy but don't really know the extent of it.
They know enough to not want to come over and I'm perfectly fine with that. The bus finally arrived, and my classmates begin to bombard the bus entrance. I always try to stand in front of the stop so I could be first and have a place to sit. I'm in luck today because after paying to get on the bus, there's two empty chairs

to my right. I immediately put my bookbag down on the first seat and sit down next to the window. Everyone boards and the bus takes off. All the other kids have a place to sit and, luckily, it's not next to me. I love having an empty seat next to me since I have a place to put my bookbag while I look out the window. My high school is about 10 minutes driving distance from my house so it's a short bus ride, but I enjoy it nonetheless. The bus route is really entertaining because it passes by these huge houses that I imagine living in. Every house is different from the next, some of them even have two stories like I've always wanted. I know it sounds repetitive, but I do enjoy looking at homes and imagining a life in them.

Fantasies are how I stay sane. I can't stand the way I live, at times I think imagining a different life is the only way I can deal with mine. Sometimes I imagine that my dad is a doctor, and my mom is a lawyer. I imagine I have two older sisters who nag me but really love me. Although this isn't my life, daydreaming about it really does help me feel better. I don't know what I'd do without my imagination, it's the light in the dark. My safe place. The school's stop is coming up, and although the bus is still moving, everyone rushes to the door. I try to be the last one to leave the bus so I can hold off on going back to reality. The stop is a fast food restaurant across the street from my high school. The bus comes to a complete stop and I watch it empty in a few seconds. Once everyone's off, I slowly get up and tell the bus driver to have a great day. I get off and cross traffic to get to start my few hours of freedom before I'm back in my hell trailer. With school not starting for 20 minutes, I walk past the front gates of my school and see the infamous "Welcome to Liberty

Senior High School" banner. "Take your headphones off!" a security guard says as I walk in. What a stupid rule, a student can't have headphones before class even starts. We are the home of the Patriots, but I honestly don't think there's anything patriotic about this school. I don't have one teacher that stands out in my mind as someone who cares about their students and actually teaches.

If I have any knowledge, it's because I stayed up and studied the subject. These teachers just come to collect a paycheck and go home. I understand they need to pay for their bills, but they are shaping future minds, they should care more. There's also a lot of favoritism when it comes to the students and staff, so I just do what I have to do and don't let any school politics get to me. I don't care to be any of their favorites. I have US history for my first period class, and I already know I'm going to dread it. Luckily, today we go to all our classes so the day goes by way quicker than block days. My first class is on the second floor, meaning I have to walk to our central plaza to take the stairs.

"Central Plaza " is the midpoint of our school. Most people hang out here before class starts or in the back of the school to get breakfast. I never did, I usually always go straight to class. If I did ever hang out somewhere in here, it was the back of the school. As I walk up, I can literally hear two teachers gossiping about a student's grade and lack of effort. Being petty, I make sure to make eye contact with both of them, showing disgust on my face to imply I heard them, and of course they both walk away. The teachers here suck. Students have real problems and not a single teacher or faculty member tries to help them. Even our own counselors belittle and giggle at students when they try to have a serious conversation with them.

I remember one time a teacher sent me to a counselor because I had too many bruises on my arms, which unknowingly to her, was because of my stepdad hitting me. The counselor told me "Well, stop messing around and get to class, come on Glend, grow up, be mature!" I mean, did she expect a 15-year-old to have the same level of maturity as a 40 year old? I guess her degree couldn't help her see a child in an abusive situation.

When I get to my class, the door is open. "Good morning, Glend. It seems you're the first one here today! Last week of class before winter break! I can't wait!!" Mr. Montez says, excited to get through the week and onto vacation. "Good morning Mr. Montez, I honestly forgot winter break is next week. I guess I can't wait either. How was your weekend?" I say as I lie through my teeth and take my seat. Oh my GOD! Winter break. I have to be home for two weeks straight. I don't know how I forgot that. The holidays are usually horrible because that's when my stepdad drinks the most. I know I can pick up a bunch of shifts at work, but still, it's not the same as the daily break Monday through Friday offers me. "It was amazing, I took my daughter to a Christmas themed park in South Miami. They had lights, rides, Santa, everything you can think of!" I can tell he had fun because he's still not done. "We had an amazing weekend, thank you for asking. You should tell your parents to take you." He says as he turns away and begins to type an email. I know it isn't his fault, since I've never mentioned my home life, but I wish he asked me how my weekend was even though I probably wouldn't tell him the truth.

Maybe he would've picked up on something being wrong. What would he say if I told him how I had to carry my mom and stepdad into bed Saturday morning? I wish he could look at me and actually see the broken distraught child right in front of him. I have to get out of my head, I feel myself getting emotional and sad. I just want someone that understands me, or at least tries to understand me. The class is starting to take their seats, so I have to hold my tears back and compose myself. I wish everyone in this room knew how much I was hurting, or how much I completely hate being home.

Chapter 2

As expected, the day flew by. Before I knew it, we were already at lunch. Lunch lasts fifty minutes then it's just two more periods and I'm "free", but only from the one place I can get away. Throughout the day, I always have mixed feelings about how fast I want the day to go. I don't really want to be home, but I don't want to be at school either. As I sat at my usual lunch table with my friends, I finally feel normal. I actually feel like a teenager. People begin gossiping about the events from the weekend, and as shallow as it sounds, it helps distract me from the horror of my life at home. I can't lie, I love chisme.

"What did you do this weekend, Glend?! Anything juicy?" Ashley asks. This weekend was so annoying but I obviously can't let anyone know. "It was pretty chill. I just went to my cousin's house in homestead and worked." I say while nervously chuckling. I rehearse my lies at home so that I don't get tongue twisted. Most of my casual friends in school don't know the whole truth, just the pieces I show them. "Ugh, you're so boring! Come spend a weekend at my house, my parents love you and we can actually go to a party! You never come out with us!" She says with a warm smile. I've gotten really close to Ashley this year. We both have English together and have hit it off really well since the beginning of the year. I've gone to her house a couple of times and her family really does love me. She truly has a beautiful life, but I can't help and be envious when I don't want to be. Honestly, many may ask themselves, why don't I just tell people what I'm going through? I would just say, I have my reasons.

Ashley lives such a happy beautiful life, she's in a bubble of perfection and I don't want to pop it with my negativity. Her life obviously isn't perfect, but she probably wouldn't understand why I feel like dying at times. I know I contradict myself, because

I say I want people to ask how I'm doing and then lie when they do ask. How can someone know there's a problem if I don't speak up? "Oh my god, let me speak to my mom about it and I'll let you know! I'll see what she says, you know how she is about me sleeping over places." I say, just to continue the conversation. She doesn't really care where I sleep but it's a good cover up. "Haha yeah, definitely let me know." She replies as we all start to get up and walk to class.

"Did you do the English homework?" she asks as we get closer to class. "Yeah I did, do you need pictures of it?" She looks relieved, "Oh my god yes, please, I completely forgot to do it. I owe you!" She says while giving me a big hug "Yeah that's fine lemme just get....wait a second....fuck! I left my phone at the lunch table. I'm gonna go get it and be right back. Tell Ms. Rodriguez why I'm running late" I say as I sprint back to the lunch table. This is not what I need right before winter break. My stepdad isn't going to buy me another one, and I'll be lucky if he doesn't put his hands on me for losing it. "Fuck, I can't lose this phone. I literally can't afford it.

Fuck, I'm stupid. I'm such an idiot." I tell myself as I frantically look for my phone. I reach the table and it's not there. I look all over the floor and the tables nearby, still nothing. I am completely distraught.

"No, why can't anything go my way?!" I need to sit down at the table and completely release all the sadness I have."God, please help me. Send me some type of sign that things will change for me. Why me? Why is it always me?" I keep repeating to myself as tears stream down my face. Losing my phone is the last straw. The flood of tears and emotions are released and I spend a few minutes just wallowing over my life. I cry for a few minutes but I eventually stop. When I'm done, there is a sense of relief. I wipe my tears and remind myself that it's not the end of the world. Well, I will have to buy a new phone, but I will get through this. I give myself a pep talk and then get myself together before walking back to class. As I was about to walk out of the lunchroom when I hear someone yelling,

"Hey are you looking for a phone?" My heart stops, I turn around and see someone running towards me. "Did you lose your phone?

Someone left one at your lunch table, so I took it to Ashley, she's really the only one I know from your group. She said it was your phone and you're probably here going crazy looking for it, so I came to make sure you know she has it" He says to my relief.

Wow, I'm in shock. What a beautiful boy, this is something out of a movie. Ask God for a sign and he shows up like my prince in shiny armor. I'm totally sure this guy was meant to cross paths with me or at least I'm going to believe that because he is so cute. "Oh my god, thank you so much. Yeah, I was going crazy looking for it. I can't believe you found it and actually gave it back. That's really nice of you. Thank you. I owe you."

I say with a smile. I really mean it, he really is nice for not stealing my phone. "You owe me? Haha that sounds interesting. Are you doing anything this weekend?" he asks.
Oh my god, is this guy really gonna ask me on a date? No guy has ever asked me on a date, this is amazing. "No, I'm totally free. Did you have something in mind?" I ask. I feel like a schoolgirl. This is it. "Yeah I actually did… Could you do my virtual school? I'll pay you." He says with no hesitation. Wow, so he's not asking me on a date. Well, I feel like an idiot. Although I'm invisible to a lot of people, he's probably heard of my side business where I do people's virtual school homework for money. It's all easy classes like Spanish or Math, and some of these kids pay big bucks to get an A or to graduate. "I have a lot on my plate right now so I don't really think I can but I can definitely let you know once I get someone else's class done. Here I'll give you my number, text me so I can have yours and I'll let you know when I can do yours.
I still owe you." This time, I'm definitely flirting. This time, I hope he picks up on it. I write down my number on a piece of paper and hand it to him. I'm trying to sound confident, but I hope he didn't pick up that I feel like he rejected me. He probably likes girls anyway. He reaches into his pocket and hands me a $20 bill.

"Here, for lunch, my treat. Think about my virtual, please. I really need it. I'll text you soon. Don't lose your phone again, I might not be here to find it!" he says as he laughs and flashes his beautiful smile.

"Haha, I'll try not to." I say as I turn around and start to walk away in the other direction. I know I'm late but I'm still in shock at the whole situation. Maybe he really was put in my path for a reason and the reason is virtual school. I mean isn't there a bible passage where God puts a man in front of a gay man to treat him? No? Wrong bible I guess. "Hurry up and get to class!" A security yells at me. "Yes, I'm on my way sorry." I say as I start to speed walk
to class. I'm about twenty minutes late, but it should be okay. I walk in and we have a substitute, yes! "Sign in for me please" I hear the substitute say. "Yes sir!" I've never been so happy and relieved. I sit next to Ashley and she turns to me. "I have your phone!! You have to be more careful, what if this kid wasn't there?" she says in a stern tone as she hands me my phone. "Yes, I am super grateful, I'm literally gonna glue this phone to my hand." I laugh as I put my phone safely in my pocket. "Thank you." I whisper. "Did you say something Glend?" Ashley asks. "No, not at all." I reply, embarrassed that she heard me. The next two periods finish in a blink of an eye. The bell rings to dismiss us but my sixth period teacher is one of those "the bell doesn't dismiss you, I dismiss you" ass bitches, you know the type. She takes two laps around the class and then says "Alright, class dismissed" as she takes a seat at her desk.

Walking towards the bus stop, I decide I'm going to take the chance to finally check my phone. When I look, an unknown number texted me an hour ago. It must be that handsome straight boy who needs me to do his homework. The message said: "Lmaoo, make sure to keep your phone safe! Enjoy lunch on me. Lmk about the virtual school please I need it to graduate, remember you owe me! Lmao, dale bro!" Fuck, I really should do his virtual since he found my phone, but I have too much on my plate right now. I texted him back saying: "Hey who's this?! Lmao just kidding, so I'm gonna work hard to finish this person's class in the next few days to get started on yours. I got you bro!"

As I walk to the bus stop, I think of ways to speed up the process for the virtual class I'm doing for this other kid. I can just turn in double the assignments in a day to finish twice as fast. I'm almost done so if I do that, I'll be done sooner than expected and I can start this kid's virtual. He's super nice, I totally want to do it for him right now. I spend the whole bus ride thinking of how I have to finish my math homework asap so I can start the virtual coursework. I'm thinking so hard I didn't even get to see some of my favorite houses on the way home. No daydreaming today, real life is just too busy.
My phone begins to vibrate and it's a message from him.
"Please bro, I really need it. Like all jokes aside. If you can't do it, lmk so I can find someone else to do it."
OMG, he's really desperate for help with his virtual, I should probably try to help asap. My phone vibrates again and it's another message from him: "And don't ask who's this ever

again! Just call me X…" Just call him X? Oh boy, this seems like it's going to be interesting... For the remainder of the week, I would come home just to try to finish this other virtual class so I can help X. Once I walk in my trailer, I would go to our kitchen bar and immediately turn the computer on. I do this every day and before

I know it, the week flies by and it's Saturday night. "Glend baby, are you busy?!" My mom asks as she walks out her room. "Yes mom, I'm trying to finish these virtual assignments before tonight, they're really important." I say as I roll my eyes. My mom has no idea what's going on in my life but at least she tries to show she cares….. not really but that's what I tell myself to help me sleep at night. "My smart baby, ok well, James and I are going to get something to eat.

We'll be back in an hour, okay? Do you want anything to eat?" She asks. I know what you're thinking and the answer to your question is yes, she is lying. She won't be back in an hour. Her and James are going to eat at this local bar and "have one drink" with their food and end up here at 2 am drunk out of their mind. "No mom, thank you, I'll just order some pizza." I say before James starts to interrupt. "Hurry the fuck up, I'm hungry!" he screams from the car. He's such an impatient bastard I hate him. You're dying so bad for some undercooked wings and greasy fries you have to be disrespectful? Fucking idiot. "I'm going dumbass, shut the fuck up!" She screams back at him. Ugh, they're so toxic on the weekends. "Alright baby, see you in an hour. Call me if you need anything. I love you." She says as she walks out. "Bye Mommy, I love you too."

I say but she already closed the door. I can honestly still hear their bickering from here, it's so annoying. My mom met James when I was 11 years old, and he's always been a sleazy guy. He's taller than both of us and much stronger. He works construction so during the week he's not so bad, it's just the weekend when he decides to unwind that changes everything. I've hated him ever since I was young for many reasons, but the biggest is that he doesn't positively encourage or influence my mom at all. I know she's with him because of the security, but sometimes he just gets so out of hand, I'd rather live on the street. I remember one day he beat my mom and I so badly that I had to call out of school for a week so that no one noticed my black eye and bruises. I work hard so that one day I can take us away from him. "And done!" I say with a sigh of relief. Honestly, it's
probably the fastest I've ever finished a virtual class. I've only had this class for two weeks and I already turned in all the assignments. All that's left is the final and that's honestly a piece of cake. I'm very proud of myself, I knew I could do it.

To avoid getting distracted while working, I leave my phone charging across the room. Scrolling through social media is fun but X needs me. Now that I'm done, I hear it ring so I run to check and immediately get disappointed. Fuck, it's not him, it's just my job. I know they're about to ask me if I can work a double tomorrow because someone called out. "Hello?" I answer, trying to sound busy. "Hey Glend! I hope you're having a good night! Could you come in tomorrow at 10:00 am instead of 4:00 pm for a double? Someone called out. I'd really appreciate it." My manager confirms what I already thought. I'm not surprised at all that someone called out, Monica is intolerable, and the store is never good enough for her. She complains and complains but never actually helps out. Oh well, money is money and I sure as hell need it. "Hey Monica, yes I'll be there tomorrow at 10 for a double. I don't mind at all, I'm always willing to help you guys." I say as I hang up. I'm really only willing to help because they're paying me but that's not the point. I need my job, so I always try to do my best to make my managers happy. Luckily, I get along with everyone at work and I enjoy that way better than being home.

I work at a popular clothing store in the mall. The job gets pretty hectic, but time goes by so fast. I'm one of the fastest cashiers so I try to get people out of the store as quickly as possible.

Customers always seem to love me and my smile. They say I'm naturally charismatic and honestly make their shopping experience a delightful one. I've even had a customer tell me that I'm going to be extremely successful one day, to not let life kick me down because my personality will take me far. I'm also the cashier with the highest rating from customer surveys so my job is always ready to give me hours.

For the next three days, I worked three doubles back-to-back. By the end of my third double, I couldn't feel my feet and my legs felt like jelly. It's Christmas Eve and everyone is doing

their last minute shopping meaning I have three times as many people in the store than I usually would. Working retail during the holidays really does tire you out. I check the clock and see it's 9:00 pm, which means I have to go! I tell all my managers I don't mind working any shift, as long as I leave by 9 pm because I have to catch the bus home. As I clock out, I wish everyone a Merry Christmas and then leave. As I approach the exit, I see Monica trying to organize a table of graphic tees.
"Merry Christmas to you and your family! Thank you for everything you do!" Monica says as she folds the tees and places them neatly onto the table.
"Thank you Monica, Merry Christmas to you and your loved ones. See you in a few days." I say with a huge smile as I walk out. Honestly, my feet were hurting pretty badly 10 minutes ago but now they're fine. Sometimes I think I'm only tired because I'm at work.

I'm just happy to be out now. I love working at the mall, especially during this time of year. Nothing feels more festive than being at the mall during the holidays. The lights, the decorations, the family shopping.

The energy amongst the people is just festive, even though there's a lot of frustration, it's a happy time of year. I love the atmosphere of it, it makes me really appreciate the little things.

As I walk across the mall to my bus stop, I take in the festive air. Passing by bickering families, I can't help but feel envious.
I wonder what it's like to have a family to buy you gifts for Christmas, or to open gifts on Christmas day as one big happy family. I usually try to spend it at a friend's house but this year I just want to go to sleep. I'm way too tired. It's Christmas Eve so I know my mom and stepdad are already drunk. Truth be told, they get twice as drunk on the holidays and Christmas Eve is like The Super Bowl of holidays for Hispanics. Especially the ones who like to drink and milk the excuse. I reach the bus stop just in time to board the bus. As I ride all the way home, I can't help but wonder how different my life could be right now. In my dream life, my mom wouldn't let me work on Christmas Eve. She'd be too overprotective. She would demand that her baby be home for the holiday.

I'd be getting ready at this time because everybody is coming over since our house would be the main gathering point for our family. When the fantasy gets so good it makes me sad, I like to snap back into reality and remind myself that although this isn't my life now, one day it will be. Maybe I won't be the son of my parents dreams, but I'll make an amazing father. Gay or not, I'll be the best father in the world to my kids.
After about an hour, we finally reached my bus stop. It looks like I'm the last person here. I get up and tell the bus driver, "I hope you have a very Merry Christmas with your loved ones." He looks at me, smiles and says, "Merry Christmas, likewise!"

As I walk through my trailer park, I see all the families gathered and parties being thrown. In fact, the trailer park feels so festive that I actually feel as happy as I do at the mall. I take the long way home just to take in all this happiness. Once I get home, I open the trailer door and see my mom and James passed out in the living room. It seems they started early today, which is great because I won't have to hear arguing, crying or fussing. I carry both of them into their bed and make sure to tuck them in. Once I clean up their mess, I decide to lay down on my couch and finally relax. All these doubles really hit me once I lay down. The trailer is actually peaceful and quiet so I'm going to take advantage to catch up on some sleep. As I start getting comfortable, my phone vibrates. I check it and it's a message from X. "Hey I'm pretty drunk. I hope you're having a fun time with your family. Please help me with my virtual, I really need you. Merry Christmas!"

Wow, the feeling of being needed really does f eel amazing. I reply right away "Hey, it's ok! I'm at my uncle's house with my family. I'll help you starting the twenty sixth. We can talk about how much when I log in! Hope you have a Merry Christmas too!" Once I hit send, my heart accelerates. Not a minute goes by, and he replies. "That's awesome! Ok, can I pick you up on the 26th so we can talk about the class and payment?!" he asks. He wants to pick me up?!

I have to be smooth and calm, I don't want him to think I like him and then he doesn't want to pay me. "Yeah of course, I'll let you know when I'm free." I reply. I make sure to look around and get some water, so I know I'm not dreaming. A few minutes go by, and I figured he isn't going to reply. I calm down and finally start letting my body rest. As I lay down, I have to remind myself he only wants virtual and nothing more. Sure, finding my phone was cute but I'm sure he's just a nice guy. This is 100% platonic. My phone vibrates one more time and of course it's him. I'm hesitant to look and when I finally open it, He said "Damn… I can't wait."

He's just a nice guy who wants nothing more than his virtual done, right? RIGHT?!

Chapter 3

I miscalculated. I spent way too much money last week and I'm officially broke. I mean, I'm normally broke, but right now I'm no money at all broke. James went to work so my mom and I have been home all day. She hasn't said anything, but I can tell she doesn't have any money either. I can hear her stomach growling from across the trailer. I hate seeing her like this. Me being hungry is one thing but her being hungry is another. X hasn't texted me since Christmas Eve, but we were supposed to meet up today, so I'll just ask him to pay me the deposit. Plus, it's a good excuse to talk to him. "Hey, are you still interested in me doing the virtual?" I ask him.

Not even five minutes pass and he replies, "Yes! I've been waiting for you all day, send me your address. I'll drop off the money now. I need this done asap." Maybe I just misinterpreted the messages, it really does look like he's only interested in me doing his virtual. I don't care either, I hit him up because I needed the money so him dropping it off is perfect. I send him my address and rush to the bathroom to make sure I look presentable. I might not care but I'm still going to look good. "Are you going somewhere?" my mom asks. "No, my friend is just dropping something off. Once he leaves, I'm going to get some food. You want some?" I turn around, happy to help. "I'll just pick at whatever you get, I'm not really that hungry. Besides, James is coming in a few hours, and he'll probably bring us food." She says trying not to sound too needy.

I know James does things like this on purpose. Why wouldn't you leave your partner some money for food? He's probably worried she'll buy me food since when she said he'll bring us food, she meant just him and her. My mom usually leaves me half of her food anyway, but he'll never bring me anything. I brush my teeth and make sure I put on some cologne.

I hate giving people my address because I know people judge my trailer or at least that's how I feel. I know I live in Miami, but a lot of these kids' parents have money, they just act hood. The only reason I told him where I live is because me and my mom really need the money. A few minutes pass by and I get the "I'm outside" message I've been waiting for. "Alright, going now." I reply. I get my phone, wallet, and headphones. "Mom, once my friend leaves, I'm going to get food okay?" I say one more time hoping she tells me what she wants to eat. "Alright my love, see you!" she says. I make sure to take a deep breath before walking out of the trailer. I may be a little bit nervous. My trailer has no cars, but he's parked on the street. I walk up to the car very slow and timid; he notices that I'm there and puts the window down.

"Hey!" I say very awkwardly. "Hey, still have your phone right?" he says with a smile. "Haha, yeah I do." Ugh I hate guys that make me laugh. "So I finally finished a few classes I was working on so I'll be able to do your class. What class is it?" I ask. "Bro, you're going to make so much fun of me but it's Spanish. I literally suck at it, and I have no time to do it. How much?" he asks.

"Aren't you Hispanic? Your parents never taught you Spanish?!" I joke around before giving him my response. "I usually charge $100 for Spanish; I need at least $25 to start and then you give me the rest when I'm done." I answer. "Damn, that's perfect, okay here's $50 and I'll give you $100 when you're done! I kinda need this done as soon as possible so I don't mind paying extra." He says as he hands me a fifty dollar bill. "You don't have to give me any more than $100, I'm going to do it and pass regardless. Thank you for the $50 though, I really appreciate it." I say with relief knowing I have money to buy food. "Text me your log in, I'll get started this weekend." I finish with a smile.

"Let me text you now so I don't forget." He says as he unlocks his phone. As I stand there waiting, my stomach starts growling. "Was that your stomach?" he asks as he puts his phone down. I'm so embarrassed, OMG! Fuck, I didn't want him to know I was

hungry. It's already late he can probably tell I haven't eaten all day. "Yeah, it was but don't worry, I'm about to walk to get some food once you leave." I say with hesitation, knowing I just put my foot in my mouth. I'm an idiot, I should've said my mom was cooking. "Bro, walk? Get in, let's go get some food."

He says, sounding more genuine than just being nice. The prideful part of me wants to tell him no but the hungry side of me is too overpowering. I get in his car and it's extremely clean, I like that.

"Where do you want to eat, maybe Mexican food?" he says as he pulls off. "Mexican food sounds good. That's my favorite" I reply. There's a Mexican spot right in front of my high school so it isn't too far from us. We don't talk much in the car, but we do make a lot of eye contact. Which is weird because a lot of guys try to avoid making eye contact with me. "Soo… do you smoke?" he asks. "No I don't actually. In fact, I suck at smoking I don't think I have the lungs for it." I say jokingly. He laughs, a little too hard. "You
suck at smoking?! That's cute as fuck, haha I've never met someone who sucks at smoking." He says as he turns into the plaza. "Haha yeah, that's me." I say while blushing. Cute as fuck? I think to myself, he knows I'm gay right? Boy you're flirting, stop. I'm sure he's just going to drop me off and call it a day. He's already done a lot and I'm sure he has plans but he's starting to spark my curiosity. As he parks, he turns to me and says, "Let's go eat inside, I'm pretty hungry too." We don't talk much as we wait in line either, he orders and then I order, nothing too crazy.
When he reaches the cashier, he tells the cashier, "Oh, and charge me for his too." I look at him kind of annoyed, I'm not a charity case. I quickly tell him, "I can pay for my own food. Tell me how much it is, and I'll give it to you right now."

He swipes his card, looks at me. "You're gonna break that 50 huh? Nope, don't worry about it. Just go pick a table, I'll get us drinks and silverware. What do you wanna drink?" He says all of this with a stern tone making me just go along with it. I can't believe this guy is being this nice to me just so I can do his virtual.

It's not that deep my guy but thank you. If only all my customers were this nice. "Get me a lemonade with no ice please"

I say, as I take our food to an empty table. I sit down and suddenly feel so relieved. Now I can really stretch this $50 until I get paid. "I've never heard someone ask for a drink with no ice, you're just full of surprises." X says as he walks up and sits down. "I promise there's much more to me than meets the eye." I joke as I begin to eat. Oh no, I'm starting to flirt back. We talk about a few topics like favorite movies, shows, activities, music, etc. We share a lot of things in common including our favorite shows. He hates that I love soda and I hate that he loves water. It's so cute. We cracked jokes about teachers and even shared our favorite anime with each other. He watches anime dubbed so I have to convince him that subbed is way better. He also showed me some new music because my taste is broad like his. He's so cute and so much like me, how have I never met him before? "I've never really heard of you before last week, have you been under a rock?!"

I say as I laugh. "Damn you really didn't know me?
I knew of you. I've even heard a few bad things about you." He says before I cut him off "Like what!?" I say with shock in my voice even though I already know a lot of people don't like me. "Some people talk about your personality, your sexual orientation, some people even called you poor which is a stupid thing to say about somebody." I stay silent. "Luckily, I didn't listen. Fuck those people, I think you're pretty cool so far. This is the most fun I've had in a really long time." He says as finishes his drink. "Yeah, people say very hurtful things but honestly I don't let it get to me.

Sometimes I feel invisible and other times I feel too seen so I try to keep to myself." I say without pausing. "I just need to be successful so I can build a future for me and my mom. Failure isn't an option for me. I don't let anyone's opinion get to me because no one walks in my shoes." I say with a little quiver in my voice. I rarely tell people things like this but I have this feeling of comfort around him. I feel safe, like he isn't judging but he really sees me.
"Wow, that's awesome, Glend. We've only been talking for a short time and honestly, I can totally see you being successful when we get older. Your future is definitely bright." He says making me feel all warm on the inside. We both look outside and see that the sun went down. "How long have we been here?!" I ask.

"Well, we got here at like 4 and it's about to be 8, I guess time flies when you're having fun." He says. Fuck, I was having so much fun I forgot I saved half of my bowl for my mom and now it's super cold and old. "This really was fun, but I have to go, I'm sure my mom's worried." I say as I put my half empty bowl in a bag.

"Damn, alright yeah let's go." He says, almost sounding disappointed. As we drive to my house, I'm just thinking about all the fun I just had. It didn't even feel like we were there for four hours. I need another four more if I'm being honest. Who knows, maybe when I'm done with his virtual we can still be friends. We get to my house, and I notice James' car isn't there and the lights are off. I'm sure my mom and James left to get food. Now I'm pissed, because I left for no reason but at least my mom is eating.
Ugh back to hell I go.

I don't want to get out of his car, but I know I have to. I can't stall much longer; I already have everything in hand so let me just get it over with. I look at X, "Well, thank you so much for everyth-…" He cut me off mid-sentence with a kiss. Yes, a kiss!

I'm shocked and excited at the same time. "I've been wanting to do this all day, I'm sorry." He says while I look at him like I just saw a ghost. I can't believe he just kissed me. I didn't think he liked boys; I definitely didn't think he liked me.

"I'm sorry if I made you uncomfortable, I just saw an opportunity and took it. I hope you're not mad." He continues, as I sit in his passenger seat speechless. OMG I have to say something, he's going to regret kissing me. I look at him and reply

"I'm not mad, I liked it." Wow, I can't believe I just said that. He's not the first boy I hooked up with but he's the first boy that's kissed me like that. This is new. Usually, I'm so quick with my words but right now, I'm stuck in my head, afraid to say the wrong thing. There's silence for about 20 seconds, I'm looking at the floor of his car while he stares out the front window.

Then he looks at me, "So what do you want to do now?" he asks, like he doesn't want the night to end either. This is my chance. I quickly snap back into myself. This boy is about to see why these girls' boyfriends know I'm hot and ready to go! I look him right in his eyes and say, "park in my driveway, let me show you." Before I could give him my sexy eyes, he was whipping his car into my driveway. Two weeks ago, I didn't know he existed. Four hours ago, we're eating as friends.

Now, the next thing I know is we're making out in his parked car. "How much fun are you trying to have?" he asks me as he turns off his car. We don't even have to exchange words after he asks. We look at each other, look at his back seat and we immediately rush to the back of his car. I can't believe this is happening. Internally I'm still in shock but I can't stop myself.

Our clothes just come right off, and I don't even notice it. He probably thinks I'm such a slut, everything he hears is true, but I don't even care. I start off right away by giving him head. As soon as I start sucking, he immediately grabs my head.
"Yeah, suck it, that's all yours..... Fuck, this is amazing.... Please don't stop...." He says in between moans. I really am enjoying this, seeing this man squirm because of me is so pleasing. "Come here, I want to fuck you." He says while simultaneously pushing me off him and laying down. I love how controlling he's being. I get on top without hesitation, sorta. His dick is pretty big, so it hurts at first but I'm a champion, so I take it.

The harder I ride, the harder he holds me. I ride for a few more minutes and then he wants to try another position. Now he's turning me around, telling me to, "try to lay down." I attempt to but it's kind of hard to do that in a car. I wish I was one of those kids with their own room on the other side of the house. I would totally risk James finding us together and beating me senseless. He's that cute to me, and I want to fuck him that badly. This boy is going to get me in trouble, I feel it already. He starts doing me from behind in a weird position, but I love it. "You like me fucking you? You like being my little bitch?"
Omg I don't even want to say anything I'm not thinking with my head right now. "Say yes to daddy." He whispers to me. Fuck!

This is so hot, I'm taking his dick but I can barely think let alone talk. "I can't hear you……say yes to daddy."

He says as he fucks me harder. "Yes….daddy….." I say in between strokes trying to take it, he probably can't even hear me. "You want daddy to cum in you?" he asks as he starts to slow down and begins stroking me passionately. "Yes daddy I want you to cum in me." I say loud and clear. What happened next I wasn't even expecting. He grabs my dick and says, "I want you to cum when I cum ok?" and starts jerking me off. All it took was a few more strokes and we both cum at the same time. The second I can feel his load bust in me I explode all over his hand. We sit there for about five minutes in complete awe. "Wow that was a lot…Do you have anything I can clean myself with?" I ask while giggling like a little schoolgirl. Omg I love him already. "Yeah, here use this spare shirt. Also, I have no idea what came over me, but I've never been with a guy before so please don't tell anyone. This is probably never going to happen again." He says as he hands me an old shirt. I'm shocked because I thought he was different, but I guess I can't be surprised. "You don't have to worry, I won't say anything."
I say as I wipe myself and we both start getting dressed. Clearly the guilt is starting to bring him back to reality. "Honestly, we had a really cool connection. I'm not gay or anything but I wouldn't mind being your friend if that's ok." He says as he reaches his hand out for a handshake. Bro,
I just had your dick in my mouth and you're giving me a handshake!? Whatever, I reach out to shake his hand. "Haha,

yeah being friends sounds awesome." I say lying through my teeth. I step out of the car and fix my clothes before beginning my walk back inside. He goes to the driver's seat and lowers the window.

At least he's not acting super weird about it. I hope he doesn't regret it or start being different with me. I remind him to text me his log in info, say goodbye and watch him drive off before finally going inside. I go in my trailer, leave my food at the kitchen bar and rush to the bathroom to take a shower. As I shower, I start replaying the entire day in my head like a love struck puppy. This is so me, to be crushing on a boy I can't have, but it's never been this bad. How did one thing lead to another? How did we go from virtual school to fucking in front of my house? Are we really just friends?

I wish I sucked his dick like we were just friends then. Ugh I have so many questions and the only one with the answers is X. How did I just lose all control of the situation? OMG. I finish my shower, brush my teeth, put some pjs on and get on my couch.

Today started so shitty but then X came and it was honestly so much fun, I want to relive it every day. X just wants to be friends, but I feel a real connection with him. In all seriousness, I know I am not in love with him, but I do know I like him. Like him, like him. As I lay there, my mind is racing. I wonder if he's thinking about me too. I wonder if he's thinking about what happened tonight. I wonder what he's thinking about in general.

Once he sends the log in for his virtual, I'm going to spark a conversation. I need to know what he's thinking. I check my phone and he still hasn't sent the log in. Hours go by, my mom and James get home drunk, without any craziness happening before they make it to bed. Wow, that's a first. They're so out of it they don't even realize I'm on the couch. I eventually fall asleep with the hopes that I'll wake up to a text message from X. The next morning, I wake up and see that he still hasn't texted me. I'm disappointed, I can't lie.

I don't like this feeling. I get up and grab a bottle of water. As I drink it, I try to reevaluate the entire situation. I'm used to "straight" guys having sex with me and ghosting me because they can't handle that they're gay. The only difference is that I don't have a connection with those guys. X is different. X and I made four hours feel like thirty minutes. I'm sure X felt it too, I mean why would he kiss me if he didn't feel something for me? Right? Times like this I wish I had a friend who I could ask or just talk to, because I feel crazy asking myself these questions.
Maybe a second opinion would help me calm down or think clearly, but I wouldn't even know who to ask. I lay back down on my couch and decide to just wait for him to text the login info.

A whole day goes by, and he hasn't texted me. He hasn't spoken to me since he dropped me off but maybe he's just busy. Ugh why can't I just not care like usual. No more dates with hot

guys. Omg was that our first date? Whatever, forget X. Since the weekend is finally here, it's time to work some doubles.
As I walk in my store, I'm ready for a dreadful shift. People who have never worked retail think that Christmas madness ends on Christmas and that's absolutely not true. Once Christmas gifts have been bought and distributed, next comes gift exchanges, gift cards and New Years outfits. As a cashier, I'm the one who has to initially deliver the bad news. "No, you can't exchange that."

"No, that wasn't bought here." "This gift card has a 0 balance." Those are the top three triggers for customers which makes them want to speak to a manager. If they think I'm mean, Monica is way worse. I try my hardest to not get Monica involved and I even try telling the customers that they're barking up the wrong tree, but they never listen. I clear out the store and decide to take my break.
The stress of my store is honestly helping me forget X exists, basically trading one headache for another. During my break, I sit down and just stare at my phone wondering why he hasn't texted me. "Oh I know that look" Monica says from across the break room. I was so focused on my phone I didn't even notice she was on break as well. "Waiting for someone to text you? Huh Glend?" She says. "Yeah, I didn't think it was that obvious, sorry." I say, embarrassed at the fact my stress over a boy is that visible. "Oh honey, it wasn't super obvious. It's just obvious to me because I see that look in the mirror sometimes." she says

with an understanding tone that actually shocks me more than X kissing me. Is this her way of trying to connect with me?
"I'm going to give you the same advice I give myself."
Oh God, I think to myself while I smile through the pain.
"Don't wait for an opportunity. If there's no opportunity, make one. I'm sure this guy is playing the same game you're playing Glend, so text him. Fuck it, life is too short." Wow, that was actually pretty good advice. I should stop being such a sour patch because of him and do something about it. "When you put it that way, you're totally right Monica thank you. I'm going to follow your advice." I reply smiling. "Good! At least you listen to me.
Hurry up and eat though, we need you on the floor." She says as she looks down and starts playing with her phone. Good old Monica. I finish eating, wash my hands and clock right back in. I decided to wait until my shift was over to text him.
The next five hours go by super fast, I blinked and I'm already clocking out, just how I like it. As I walk out, I see Monica organizing some jeans."Remember Glend, make the opportunity. Good night, see you tomorrow!" she says. "Good night Monica, see you tomorrow!" I say as I speed walk out of the store. I reach the bus stop and it's already there, so I just quickly find my seat. I tell myself that I have to make a decision in five minutes. Either I'm going to text him or I'm not, but I'm done worrying about it. So naturally time slows down and the next five minutes feel longer than my whole shift. What's wrong with just texting him? I'm not even trying to talk just yet, all I'm going to do is ask for his login info. Good pep talk. Alright, I'm going to do it. I type "Hey! You never sent me the log in. I need

it to start" and hit send. I wait patiently and think of all the possible responses he can give, even though he's probably just going to send the info.

Ten minutes go by and no response. Then, twenty minutes… then thirty. Before I know it, I'm already walking home, and he still hasn't sent a response. He already paid me, why is he avoiding me like this? I know I'm overthinking this, but I can't help it. Did I text him too late? Maybe he's really busy? Maybe someone has his phone? There are so many possibilities that it's making my head explode. I finally reach my driveway and see James and my mom aren't home yet. I unlock the door and come inside to an empty, dark trailer. I don't know why, but today it feels extra depressing. It's not because of X, he was just a onenight escape from it. As I'm ordering pizza, I get a message from him. I get so nervous I hang up on the pizza place. I can't even think. When I open the message, it reads, "Hey, I don't need you to do my virtual anymore. I found someone else. Keep the $50.

Thanks anyways." I stare at that message long and hard. That's all you have to say? Seriously? Nothing else? I'm not even going to respond. X is confused and I definitely don't need this in my life right now. I need to focus on getting ahead. Let me order my pizza and forget all about him.

Chapter 4

The next few days weren't easy, I kept catching myself randomly thinking of him. At work, I hoped he would walk in. When I buy Mexican food, I would stare at the table we had our long convo at. Honestly, every time I pass my driveway I think of him. On New Years, I wanted to text him, Happy New Year, but I decided not to. It's easier to just keep my mind focused and to forget him. I looked at the positives, I got free food, $50 and dick. It's the first day back from winter break and I'm actually excited. I'm walking to class as happy as can be. As I walk up the stairs of Central Plaza to my first period, I see X and a girl walking by holding hands so it's safe to assume that's his girlfriend. As we pass each other, X and I make eye contact. I honestly don't know what I feel. A sense of relief, but at the same time, confusion.

Am I hurt? I walk to class with the mindset that X and I will never speak again. It was a good night, but nobody's worth the headache. As I sit down, I say Hi to Mr. Montez. "How was your winter break?" I ask even though I don't care all I can think about is how X really has a girlfriend now. As he rambles on about how he had a beautiful vacation, my phone vibrates. It's a message from X "We need to talk in person. Let me know when you're free." I sit there while I hear Mr. Montez in the background. I'm way too confused. I don't know what to do. Where's Monica when you need her?! Every time I'm in class, I realize how little these teachers actually teach me. They really just come to this building to collect a paycheck because no one in my English class knows what's going on.

My English teacher, Ms. Rodriguez, can't spell and I want to correct her so badly, but I refrain so I don't embarrass her. Luckily the school day is almost over and today I would rather be in my trailer than this school. It's the first Monday of the new year and I'm already so stressed. I wonder what X wants to talk to me about. I just thought we weren't going to talk anymore, and I really didn't think if we did talk, it would be quick. Honestly, that would be easier. I'm stressing harder today than I was when I was going to send that text. Well Monica, I sure as hell made an opportunity. An opportunity to get played with and made a fool of. Ms. Rodriguez walks out to flirt with the next door teacher and the students begin to talk amongst themselves. Ashley turns around and asks "How was your winter break Glend? Get anything cool for Christmas?" She doesn't let me answer before she says, "My parents gave me $1000 and a new phone. I really wanted a car, but my dad said I'll get it when I graduate." Her smile was so big, I couldn't hate on her, but wow, I wish. I have to save to buy my own car and honestly, I don't even know how to drive. James doesn't want to teach me."It was good. Saw the family, worked a little. My mom gave me $800 and said to just go buy what I want haha." I say hoping she believes me. It was a total lie, my mom didn't get me anything. I actually gave her $100 so she can eat when James isn't there, or to buy anything she needs.

"Aw at least you got to spend it with your family. You

should've come with me to this party on Saturday, it was so much fun! You remember that kid who found your phone?" she asks.

Oh my god, she means X! "I think I do; I vaguely remember him. Why what's up?" I ask knowing he just fucked me over winter break. "He was at the party on Saturday and walked in with

Britney! I guess they're talking now because she got way too trashed and he took care of her the whole night. They were like kissing up on each other and everything. Honestly I didn't even know what to say. His mom and my mom are friends, so I've known him for a really long time, it's weird seeing him kiss a girl haha." She says giggling. If there's one thing Ashley has, it's good gossip. "Weird because you like him or?" I ask, trying to hide my true intention behind my curiosity. I know he's not the kind of guy Ashley goes for but let's see what she says.

"Ew! Wtf no, he's not my type at all. I honestly see him like a little cousin. I could never." she rolls her eyes and continues, "He could do way better than Britney though. She's like nasty." She says with a look of disgust in her eyes.

"I think I saw them this morning and they look pretty happy. Who knows, looks can be deceiving." I say pretending I'm impartial to the subject. He could do so much better than Britney. He could be with me.

"Oh Glend, you're so innocent. He's obviously using her to get someone's attention. I'm gonna find out who and let you know. This is too juicy to let go." She says as she turns back around.

Ms. Rodriguez walks back in and continues her lesson.

I couldn't help but think about what Ashley said. I have two questions. Could it be that he's using Britney to get someone jealous? And is that someone me? The day ended quickly and before I knew it I was back on the bus on my way home. The whole ride the two questions kept replaying in my head.

It would make sense, after all, X is way too cute for Britney. But who does he want to make jealous? As I walk into my trailer, I see my mom watching tv in the living room.
"Hey Glend! How was school? You have fun? Learn anything?" she asks. I wanna say boring, no and no but let me not get her started. "School was fun mom, I did learn a lot. Hopefully tomorrow comes sooner!" I say. There's no way she actually thinks I'm serious, but I don't think she cares enough to pay attention. "I made some food, I left your plate in the fridge. Want
me to warm it up for you?" she asks. "Yeah that would be awesome mom, thank you." I reply. These little moments are something I really do appreciate. Seeing my mom warm up my food and serve me a cup of soda actually makes me feel kind of normal. Especially since James isn't here, I feel way more relaxed and comfortable. "You know I love you so much right? You're my baby. I can't imagine life without you. It's always gonna be just me and you okay?" She says as she gives me a kiss on the forehead. "I love you too mommy, just me and you." I say as I start to eat. Wow, I feel so loved and appreciated

today. I love when my mom talks to me like that. She doesn't do it very often because James gets jealous, so when she does it, it makes it ten times more special.

My mom goes to her room while I hurry to finish eating so I can go lay on my couch and attempt to relax. I haven't responded to X and I don't know if I should. What's there to talk about? We had a connection, we had sex and then we come back from winter break, and he has a girlfriend. It's confusing but that's the reality.

I stare at my trailer ceiling wondering what I should do. "I'm not going to text him. He has a girlfriend." I say to myself. After repeating that to myself over and over, I feel a weight being lifted off my shoulders. Next thing I know I wake up to my phone vibrating. I look at the time and I've been sleeping for two, much needed hours. When I look to see who's calling me, it's X. My heart drops. He's called me 15 times and left me a bunch of text messages. Just when I was about to look at them, he calls me for the sixteenth time. "Hey what's up?" I answer. "Oh my god, you finally picked up. I've been blowing up your phone. I'm sorry I just got really anxious. Can we talk in person please?" he blurts out without giving me a chance to speak. It really does sound like he's been going through it while I was sleeping. "Sure, come to my house, I guess we can talk in your car." I say. "Perfect, I'll be there in 5 minutes." He says then he hangs up. Umm five minutes!? Was he at the entrance waiting for me already? I immediately rush to the bathroom and see that my mom and James are just laying down watching tv.

"Are you going somewhere Glend?" my mom asks. "I'm just going to talk to a friend about some homework. I'll be back in a little" I say as I start brushing my teeth. I constantly brush my teeth because since I barely eat, my breath smells really bad at times. I make sure to wash my face, put on some cologne and freshen up. I get the "I'm outside" text a few minutes later and rush to meet him in his car. I get in the car, and he immediately looks sad.

"Can we please talk?" he asks. "Sure, but what's there to talk about? Don't worry I won't tell your girlfriend we had sex. I'm not going to tell anyone if that's what you're worried about. It wasn't a big deal" I say trying to put him at ease. His face looks very surprised as I finish talking but he looks more shocked than relieved. "Wow.. so it wasn't a big deal? You didn't feel that connection? Because I did. I can't stop thinking about you. Honestly, I wanted to talk to you all day. Those four hours we spent eating made me so happy. I haven't had that type of genuine conversation in a long time. How can you say it wasn't a big deal!?" He rants as my face has his same shocked expression. I feel like he's being genuine, he seems vulnerable, and his eyes are getting watery. Granted, it was just one day but it meant a lot to the both of us. I haven't stopped thinking about him since that day.

I haven't felt that type of comfort with anyone in my entire life. I'm pretty sure he hasn't either from the way he's talking.

Every bone in my body told me to stay firm and lie but I just couldn't. "I did feel the connection and I haven't been able to stop thinking about you either. It got me really sad that you just ignored me and then I got back to school and saw you with your girlfriend. I'm sorry X but I can't be your side piece while you have a girlfriend." I say, trying to sound as firm as possible even though I would totally be his side piece. He took a long pause and says, "Glend, I'm not really with her. I don't know how to express these feelings I have for you.

I've never been with a guy, so I need to confirm my sexuality to myself. I don't think I'm gay, but I really do like you. I'm only with Britney so no one suspects that I'm gay." That's so lame to me, but whatever. I don't want to push him away, and I want him to trust me. So I'm going to keep entertaining him.

"Why would anyone think you're gay?" I ask. "Bro, I left here and I felt like everyone just knew I just did something with a guy.

It was like an internal thing. I don't know why I did it but I'm going to break up with Britney soon. I haven't even fucked her." He says as he leans over and grabs my hands. "I haven't fucked

anyone since you and I want to keep it that way. Please just be mine and
I'll be yours. I'll handle Britney in a few days and then we'll be good. We'll just be super lowkey. Ok?" he says as he begins to kiss my hands. Omg this boy is too smooth. I know it's trouble but
I don't pull my hand away.

"I haven't stopped thinking about you, Glend, please believe me. Be mine...please..." he says. Honestly, I wish I was strong enough to say no to him but I'm not. I wish I had the willpower to tell him that this is wrong. I need the courage to tell him that if we do this, we're horrible people and we're pieces of shit. I thought long and hard and finally said, "Let's find somewhere to park." I guess I'm a piece of shit too, but he's being so sweet right now I just can't help myself. He's saying all the things I wish he said since he ghosted me. That night was the beginning of something special. January 2013 was one of our first milestones. For the entire month, I got into this routine.

Wake up, go to school, come home, do my homework, get picked up by X and then get my brains fucked out of me by him in whatever parking spot we found. If I wasn't waking up for school, I was waking up for work. Either way, I was getting picked up and fucked by X at night. It also wasn't just sex; our emotional bond grew so much more. Every day, we talked for hours just like our first encounter. Sometimes, we'd spend the

whole night driving and talking. I showed him PH, the houses I imagined I lived in, the made-up scenarios that motivate me. I even went as far as to tell him about my relationship with my mom and James.
I never tell anyone how I live at home, because I don't want to be judged, but I trust X. Honestly, it feels great telling someone about it. It's a weight I'm constantly holding on my shoulders, and he didn't seem to judge me at all. He also made sure the sharing was mutual by telling me about his family and his dreams.

Every family has their ups and downs, but his family seemed pretty normal for the most part. Caring mom, overprotective dad, and annoying siblings. Usually, when someone tells me about their family life, I get a sense of envy, but not with X. His family wants him to go to college and become an accountant, but he doesn't really see himself doing that. There are so many fun facts about him. X loves clothes and says he would like to be a designer one day. X wears something black in every outfit. He loves dogs and hates cats. He hates large crowds but loves concerts. He hates avocados but loves guacamole.

It's confusing to everyone but me. He's a walking question mark, and I feel like I'm the only one with the answer.
There's definitely much more to him than meets the eye. He's my little baby. The month of January was so perfect it felt like a dream. I really don't want to wake up. I don't even hate waking

up in my trailer every morning. I'm on my way to work right now and I'm happy because I know after my shift I'll be seeing my boo. "You seem really happy, Glend." Monica says as she organizes the colognes and perfumes. "Really? Haha, I'm glad my happiness is noticeable." I say with a smile while clocking in.

"Ahh, with that smile, I'm pretty sure you're in love. Well, best of luck to you two. He's a very lucky guy." She says. I won't admit it to her, but I can't believe you can tell someone is in love just by a smile, that's insane.

"Thank you Monica, you've made my day." I say as I get ready to start doing what I have to. Today is the second day of February and since it's the first Saturday of the month, my store has to reorganize all the clothes to make space for our new shipment. Luckily, I'm a cashier so I just have to make sure to ring people out as fast as possible and fix up the products in front of my register. The day goes by so quickly that before I knew it, my shift was over. I clock out and wait in the breakroom. "Hey I'm out, are you still coming to get me?" I text X making sure everything is still good. Not a minute passes and I get his response.

"I'll be there in 15 minutes babe, I'll let you know when I'm outside" he replies. Just like that, I feel butterflies all over my stomach. "Ok thank you babe" I write back.

Honestly, having him call me babe is such a rewarding

feeling. It's something I've been looking for my entire life. I know I'm young but ever since Middle school I watched my peers date and wanted those same things. He said he'll be here in 15 minutes so I might as well start heading out and wait for him at our spot. As I walk towards the exit of the store, Monica yells from behind the register. "Bye Glend, have fun tonight…but not too much fun!" she laughs jokingly. I turn around, and wave briefly. "Bye Monica, good luck with all the inventory and I'll try not to!" I reply walking out of the store. As I pass by a bunch of people in the mall, I can't help but wonder if they can all see how truly happy and in love I am. I'll be honest, this is the first time I've ever felt like this about a guy. Guys usually only use me to fuck, and I normally don't mind, but X fucks me while having a true emotional connection with me. He's gotten to know a side of me that I never thought existed.

Once I reach our spot, he's already there waiting for me. He usually picks me up in an empty parking lot so no one really sees, but I don't care. I know we can't be exactly like everyone else, but I don't care. It's still such an amazing feeling to have your man waiting to pick you up. I get in the car and immediately give him a kiss. "Well, hi to you too, how was work babe?" he asks. "Work was awesome, we're replenishing the floor, so I have to be quick with ringing people out." I say. "Damn, that must be hectic but I'm sure you got this. My baby can do anything." He says as he begins to drive me home. He's always saying little sweet things like that. On the way home, I ask him for a phone charger, and he says to look for it in his glove compartment.

“It’s way too dark.” I say as I turn on the light. I look for less than two minutes and finally find it.“Did you find it?” he asks.

“Yeah I did, thanks babe.” I say as I reach to turn off the light. In less than a second, I see an unusual mark on his neck. “What’s that spot on your neck?” I ask. “What’s on my neck?” he asks in a very serious tone, almost too serious. “That’s a hickey” I say since he wants to play stupid. “Are you sure it’s a hickey?” he asks with a confused tone making the situation worse. “Well, I’m not fucking stupid, I know what a hickey looks like. Of course it’s a hickey.” I rudely say getting angrier by the moment. “Alright calm down, you don’t have to curse at me. You probably gave it to me. What’s the big deal?” he says. I can feel myself becoming embroiled with anger. “Don’t tell me to calm down. I don’t give you hickeys, we’re lowkey remember!? I know that wasn’t me.

Who gave you a hickey?” I shout as we reach our exit.

He’s silent for two minutes and turns to me and says, “Britney gave it to me, I’m sorry.” As he stares at me, tears start streaming down his face. This time the water works doesn’t have the same effect. Once he says that, my perfect happy bubble pops and I’m immediately humbled. I have to take a few moments to gather my thoughts. I calmly ask him, “Can you please keep your eyes on the road, I want to get home safely.” I wish that’s all I said to him, but I can’t just not say anything. He has a fucking hickey. “If you’re only fucking me, how did she give it to you?”

He continues to drive but he begins crying hysterically. "I'm sorry,
I'm so sorry. It happened one time and I didn't even finish, I swear.

I didn't want to bring it up to you because I didn't want to hurt you. Please believe me baby. I'm such a fuck up, I fuck everything up!" he yells in between sobs. Honestly, I sit there for the rest of the car ride watching his breakdown and I can't help but judge. He's really going to start crying and being all dramatic simply because he got caught? That's so stupid and unattractive. He looks like a child in a supermarket, mad because their parents won't buy them candy. Had I not caught him, he wouldn't feel
like such a fuck up. He wouldn't feel guilty at all. His little act is transparent as fuck. I'm silent the rest of the car ride. Once we reach my house, I take a deep breath and finally say something. "I'll be honest, I don't really believe you. I'm hurt, but I should've expected something like this was going to happen.

It was somewhat inevitable I'm done with our little make believe relationship." I'm keeping my composure but I'm definitely holding back my tears. This hurts more than anything I've ever experienced but I can't let him see me weak. I want him to see how serious I am, he can't do this to me. He grabs my hands and says "We were doing so perfect babe, please don't leave me. Please, I'm sorry, I'm a fuck up I know, it will never happen again." He pleads and pleads, saying different variations of the same lies. Honestly, ninety-nine percent of me wants to forgive him, but that one percent just doesn't let me. I need to set some respect for myself. "I know you have a girlfriend and I agreed to keep seeing you, but you were the one who told me that you weren't fucking her. Not only that, when I caught you with the hickey, you tried to make it seem like I gave it to you.

You tried manipulating me X. I honestly thought I knew you, but I clearly don't. I'm sorry we're done." I say as I snatch my hand away from him and step out of his car. As I walk away, I hear him punching his steering wheel. Whenever a man is guilty of something, he punches his steering wheel. That should be one of Newton's Laws. I open the door and luckily no one is home. I put my bag down and run over to my couch, I need to lay down and close my eyes. While I was in the car, I was holding the tears back but now that I'm home, I feel nothing. I'm completely numb. I stare at the ceiling and try to process what just happened. This morning, X and I were together and now we're not. Why would he hurt me? What else has he lied about?

How many times did he actually fuck her? So many questions are circulating my brain. It all seems like a cruel joke. I can't help but wonder if I deserve this. I hate Britney but she has no fault in this, she's completely innocent. I'm the antagonist who's ruining their relationship. I probably do deserve this. As I lay on my couch, the numbness overcomes my entire body. I lay there alone and numb in a sea of regret.

Chapter 5

I saw the sun rise that morning from the corner of my eye. I haven't spoken or moved in hours, just laying on my couch with no intention of ever getting up. There's not a single aspect in my life that's normal, and worst of all, I can't even ask anyone for advice. I'm way too prideful to be judged, and no one is going to know how I feel or how to help me. I can't help but wonder, why would he do this to me? I feel my bladder about to explode so I decide to go use the restroom. As I walk back, I look for my phone and I can't find it anywhere. This is not what I need right now. As I'm thinking where I could've left it I realize it's charging in X's car. Fuck, how the fuck am I supposed to get it back? I told myself I'm never talking to him again and now I definitely have to. I pace back and forth trying to figure something out. My mom and step dad aren't even here so I can't use their phone. I look at the time and it's 7 in the morning. I can ask my neighbor to let me borrow his phone, they usually treat me very nicely since I always help with the electronics in their house and they're definitely awake at this time. I'm still in my work clothes, so I quickly shower to avoid looking and feeling disgusting. I look at myself in the mirror once
I finish brushing my teeth and tell myself, "You got this, it's just a bump in the road." I'm on the verge of losing it so I need to be really positive with myself right now.

I open my door and before I even get to my neighbor's house, I look to my right and see that X's car is still in the same parking spot. I walk up to the car and see that he fell asleep.

I knock on the window and he jumps. "What are you doing here?" I ask him. "Good morning to you too haha. After you left, I realized you left your phone and I felt bad just leaving it on your porch, so I decided to wait here until you left." He says after lowering his window and handing me the phone. Wow, that was actually really sweet but that doesn't fix anything. I'm still hurt but honestly, looking at him melts my heart. He looks so perfect in the morning, how is that even possible?! I hate that I love him so much. "That was very thoughtful, thank you. You should probably get going, your parents and girlfriend are probably super worried." I say as I put my phone in my pocket. I know that was petty but fuck him. "I'm sorry I lied to you, but this is all still so new to me. I don't really know what I'm doing.
If you give me another chance, I promise I'll never lie to you again. Whatever we have, I really do want to make it work. This can't be the end of us, it's just a bump in the road." He says as his eyes get watery again. Wow, a bump in the road? Barely two months and this kid knows me too well. He knows how to talk to my personality. I know boys cry to get their way too, but I love that he gets so emotional over me. I honestly get butterflies when
I see him even though I'm extremely mad at him. But am I really?

I know I'm mad at him but I'm still so happy to see him. This is horrible.

"I don't hold grudges, so I forgive you, but I'm just
going to need some time to get over everything. Okay? Just give me some time and I'll hit you up when I'm ready. That's the best
I can do at the moment." I say with no hesitation.

We both stare at each other for a few minutes until he
finally says, "Alright, at least that's something. I won't bother you but the second you're ready, call me because I'll come flying."
Ugh that was so sweet, but I can't let him see me melt. "This gives me some type of hope because almost losing you made me realize
I need you." He says as he turns his car on. "Thank you. I'll call you when I'm ready, get home safely." I say as I walk back towards my trailer. Once I'm inside, I decide to look at my phone and see what I've missed. A few missed calls and text messages, one of the messages are from my mom saying she won't be back until Monday, so at least I have the trailer all to myself. I don't work today, so I'm just going to spend the day relaxing because I definitely deserve it. As I watch tv, I ask myself if I should give
X another chance. People make mistakes, right? I mean he's telling me he needs me, I'm pretty sure he doesn't need her. He's just using her when I'm not there. He's using her so

nobody knows the truth. On the other hand, he lied to me. He should be completely honest with me as I am with him. I can't even focus on my show, my mind is filled with so many arguments it feels like a courtroom. Over the next couple of days, all I did was think about the situation and what I should do.

Whether it was school, home, work or even the bathroom, I thought of every possible defense for and against X and the outcome of taking him back. Instead of everyone noticing how happy I was, now everyone's noticing how pensive I am. I feel like my body is on auto pilot and all I do is think.

The days seem repetitive at this point. Day in and day out, all I do is think about X and how he hurt me. How not talking to him is hurting me. So today I woke up and decided I'm tired of thinking. I've been thinking about this for almost two weeks. I told myself I need a sign to be with him. Right before I walk out the door for school, my mom turns around and says, "Good morning,
Glend, how'd you sleep? Happy Valentine's Day!" with a smile. Is today really Valentine's Day? Wow where have I been? I look at my polo and realize I'm already wearing a red one so I guess I subconsciously knew haha I love love. "Happy Valentine's Day mom. I slept great, I just have a lot on my mind." I say as I reach for my keys in my bookbag. "Ahh, you're too young to be stressed. Look baby, whatever it is, don't worry about it because it's just a bump in the road. You got this." She says as she cooks

James his breakfast. I look at her in awe, like she just said the most profound thing I've ever heard. This is the sign I've been looking for. "You're absolutely right mom, thank you. I really needed this.
See you later!" I say, walking and ready to have a good day. As I walk to the bus stop, I think about the sign my mom unknowingly gave me.

This is just a bump in our story, but we're not done. I want to be with him and even though he's publicly with Britney, the one who he truly wants to be with is me. I'm officially ready to call him but I don't want to do it yet just in case he's taking Britney to school. The day is filled with love. Every teacher has a corny Valentine's Day related lesson, and everyone is wearing red. This Valentine's Day seems extra festive or maybe this year I'm in the spirit because of X.

Just as lunch is almost over, Ashley is telling me how she's going on a date tonight with some guy she really likes. "He's sooo cute Glend. He's tall and he's a baseball player from Goldenman. He says he has the whole night planned so I'm extra excited. If we get more serious, I totally want you to meet him." I smile at her but didn't have much to say. I can't even be in public with my man."I just realized you never really talk about guys. So, what are you doing tonight? Do you have a little valentine's boo?" she asks. If she only knew her fake cousin is the guy who fucks my brains out." To be honest, I was going to do homework and maybe watch a corny love movie. I'm not really seeing anyone, so it looks like I'm taking myself out on a date haha." I say as we throw our trays away. "Aw, that's cute too. Self-love is super important. One day you'll find love and I'm going to be so excited!" She says as she jumps. Ashley really is such a nice and bubbly person. I love her energy.

"Haha yeah, one day but for now, I'll focus on me." I say as we walk to class. The truth is I've already found love and it confuses me. I walk beside Ashley and I wish I could tell her everything and see what she has to say. Maybe if I tell her without using his name, she'll be able to still give me general advice. It's worth a shot right? "Hey Ashley, can I ask you something?" I ask as we head to class."Yeah of course, what's up?" she responds.
"It's just that I…" and right before I was about to say it, I hear somebody screaming from behind us.

"Omg! Excuse me!" I turn around and it's Britney. "Am I in your way? You just interrupted our conversation. You know you can walk around us right?" I snap at her rudely. "I know, I know I'm sorry, Glend! My boyfriend is taking me out to a nice dinner tonight and I'm just nervous. I didn't mean to be so rude; I just have nothing to wear." She says as she tries to apologize. "I've been going crazy all day, I'm going to the mall after school to find an outfit." Does this bitch think I care?
"Wait! Are you guys free?! Omg, would you guys come to the mall with me?!" She says with a huge smile. Ashley and I

immediately look at each other and say "No sorry we have plans" at the same time. "Ugh, you guys suck! Excuse me, I need to find someone to help me." She says as she storms off. "Wow, what a handful right?!" Ashley says as she rolls her eyes. "Yeah, she doesn't even talk to us. Why would she even want us to go with her? That's awkward." I say trying to hide my disgust.

Ashley and I finally get to class when she says, "I hope you get that jittery about a guy one day Glend just don't be as annoying as Britney." That was so nice and thoughtful. "Thank you Ashley, let's hope so…" I say as we enter class.As I walk home after school I can't help but think about how happy and excited Britney was. It's like the universe knows what I'm thinking about because in that moment, I get a message. I already have a feeling it's X, at least I hope. I grab my phone and see that I'm right. "Hey, I'm sorry about everything. I'm hurt I can't see you today. I wish I was going to dinner with you.

Happy Valentine's Day, I love you." Honestly, these words make me feel sad. I can't believe he's going out to eat with her and I'm stuck alone on Valentine's Day. He loves me yet he's taking his girlfriend out to dinner. It just makes me feel so stupid. I get to my trailer and notice it's completely empty. It seems my mom and my stepdad are out already, enjoying their Valentine's Day. Well at least that makes one of us. I just hate that everyone gets to be with who they want except for me. I hop

in the shower and just start thinking of everything. Why is it such a big deal to be gay? Why can't people just be honest? What's the
point of hooking up with someone that can't accept their sexuality? I guess that last one is a jab at me. X told me we would be a secret and I was fine with it. That's my fault. As I wash my hair I continue to think about the complexity of men. Men are bound to curiosity and that's what leads them to trying to do sexual things with other men.

I remember my freshman year of high school I did something sexual with six out of the eleven soccer players of my school. After that, I started to believe that sixty percent of men have tried something sexual with other men. It always starts off with "so how does gay sex feel like?" or "It's just head right?" I feel like gay men are always being accused of manipulating men but who questions the straight man that comes for us? Throughout high school, I have always been a man's fantasy. So many men have used me to discover their sexuality and I'm more than happy to help, but that doesn't mean it's not frustrating. X probably thinks he's the only one but he's not.

Men love me and I'm here to please them. I spent the rest of my Valentine's Day on my couch watching tv and trying to distract myself. Unfortunately, daytime television loves reminding everyone that it's Valentine's Day. Two cheesy movies later, I notice just how late it is. I look at my phone and I start to wish that I had a missed notification from X but all I see is a blank screen. “Fuck him and fuck Valentine’s Day.” I say to myself as I roll my eyes. I turn the tv off and try to go to sleep but my stomach begins rumbling. I get up and try to look in the kitchen but there’s nothing. “I guess she forgot to leave me food, shocker.” I say as I close the fridge door. My stomach doesn’t stop rumbling so I change into something comfortable and decide to walk towards a local fast-food restaurant. I’m sure a few cheap tacos will be enough to satisfy my hunger. As I walk to get food, I realize I have to shower again when I get home. I’m going to get sweaty twice in one day.

The walk takes me about 20 minutes, but I don’t mind at all. As I walk by the houses, I imagine what having a normal life must be like. I imagine parents that don’t allow their kids to go out on school nights but make exceptions on days like today. I imagine my dad being really overprotective, strict, and wanting me home by a certain time. Even though I’m a boy, I’m his baby boy so he has to take care of me. I look at my phone, hoping my mom sent me a message asking if I’m alright, but she hasn’t. She’s living her best life with my stepdad so who am I to intrude? I cross a large street and finally reach the taco place. I walk in and immediately feel the cool air.

I’m instantly relieved and in a better mood. It’s completely empty so they were ready to take my order. I pay for it then I wait to grab my food. As I begin to walk to the door, a familiar face walks in.“Glend?” he asks. I take my headphones out and

realize it's a boy named Matias. "Yes, Hey how are you? Matias, right? Happy
Valentine's Day!" I respond, trying to be friendly and hide my disdain for today. Matias goes to another high school but since we have mutual friends, we're always around each other at parties. "Haha only my parents call me that so call me Matt. Also, Happy Valentine's Day. Honestly? I could be better bro. My girl and I broke up so I'm spending today completely alone. I was going to go through the drive thru, but I had to use the bathroom. What are you doing here?" he asks with a concerned look. "I suddenly got hungry so I walked to get some food.

I don't have any plans today either, fuck this holiday honestly." I say with a bit of my anger coming out. Matt starts to chuckle, "Yeah I feel that. Let me just order some food and I'll take you home. It's not like I'm in a rush to go anywhere." I usually don't let people take me home, but I don't feel like walking back, so I respond with, "Yeah, that actually sounds awesome." Matt eventually gets his food and we both walk to his car. I guess I should be happy I got a ride home. Matt is a life saver right now. As we get in, Matt realizes he doesn't even know where I live. Not many people do. "Let me know how to get to your house, I'm not too familiar with this area." He says. We get in and I guide him towards my house. "So how's school?" he asks. I can't believe I have to have these little stupid convos all the way home.

I need a car immediately. “School is great, can’t complain. You?” I ask to be polite. I really hope he takes the hint that I really don’t want to talk, I just want to go home. I’m annoyed as fuck that this is how I’m spending my Valentine’s Day. “Now that you mention it, school has me stressed. Matter of fact, everything has me stressed. I feel like a walking ball of stress. I feel like no one really knows what I’m going through, but no one cares enough to ask.

You get what I mean?” he says. Honestly, this is the first time I’ve heard someone else say something like that. I know exactly what he means.

“Yeah, I totally understand. Life is stressing but I never let it get to me. I always move forward.” I say knowing that is exactly what my current problem is. He looks at me and says, “Yeah I think we should all move forward.” He continues driving until we reach a red light. Thank God the small talk is over, or so I thought. While we are there in the car waiting at the light, Matt looks over to me and says, “You ever been with a girl?” I immediately turn to him and ask, “You don’t think that’s kind of intrusive?” He chuckles nervously and says, “I was just trying to make conversation, my bad bro.” Out of all the topics, that’s what he uses? What a tool. I take a deep breath and say, “No I haven’t, have you ever been with a guy?” I know he’s going to say no, but I wanted to see his reaction. He starts laughing and says “Nahhhh, I’m not bout that bro. You’re a trooper.”

As he laughs, he starts tapping my thigh. Omg this boy does not know who he is playing with. “The light’s green and my house is that way.” I say with a smile. We enter my complex and Matt begins to rub my thigh. “So Glend, what’s it like, getting with a guy?” I already know where this is headed, so I’m about to have some fun with him. I immediately look in his eyes and say, “I can show you better than I can tell you. Bout?” He continues to rub my thigh and says, “Yeah, I’m curious now… show me.” Curiosity strikes again. These boys are so easy. We drive to an empty parking lot in my complex. “Are you sure you want to try?” I turn to him and ask. I want to make sure before I have another confused guy acting weird with me.

“I’m just really intrigued. I want to try it but please don’t tell anyone.” He says. Duh, does he think I want people to know? “I promise I won’t tell anyone.” I say. “Good bitch, let’s go.” He says as he gets up and leads me to the back of his car. He plays some music as I sit on him, and we just start passionately making out. I begin to take my shirt off and eventually all of our clothes are off. “Now suck it like it yours.” He says. I start giving him the wettest blowjob I’ve ever given. I think my anger and sadness over

X was fueling the passion in my head. “Oh baby, just like that.” He moans. He grabs my hair and starts fucking my face. I feel him in the back of my throat, and it feels amazing. “Damn, you have a nice throat. Are you tight?” He asks as he grabs me around my neck. I pull his dick out of my mouth and start jerking it off.

"Yes,
I'm tight" I say as I stare into his eyes.

"Alright good, take your pants off and make daddy cum." He says, as he positions himself for me to ride his dick. I sit on him and feel him go completely inside of me. I struggle at first, but I eventually get it all in. "Damn baby, you are tight.
Fuck, ride this dick, make daddy cum baby." He says in between moans. As I ride him, all I can think about is how amazing this feels. No feelings, no attachments, no girlfriend, just Matt fucking me like the dirty bitch I am. "Let me fuck you doggy." We switch positions, and he begins to fuck me while I'm on all four in his back seat. He's kissing my neck while fucking me and telling me that I better not tell anyone. That this better be our little secret.
That I'm his little bitch, and the more he calls me his little bitch, the more I'm turned on.

"You want me to cum in you baby? Say you want my cum, say it loud." He says as he strokes faster and faster. "Yes daddy, I want your cum." I scream out. His strokes get faster and faster until he finally busts inside me. I can feel him pulsing. As Matt pulls out of me he takes a few minutes to collect his thoughts and he says, "wow, I've never done something like that before. I'm not gay or anything but wow, you're awesome." Same old story. I'm only seventeen, is this all I have to look forward to? As I put my clothes on, I can't help but chuckle. "I wouldn't say amazing, but I get the job done right? Haha." I say

as I buckle my pants. "Yeah, it was good but please don't tell anyone and we can do this again." He says as he jumps to the driver seat. Do it again?
"Ok, can you take me home now? I'm starving haha."

Matt begins to drive and as we approach my house, he turns to me, gives me a kiss and asks, "didn't you have enough meat?" with a huge smile. What a flirt. I kiss him back and say, "I'll never have enough meat." I get out of the car and Matt lowers the window and says, "Don't tell anyone about this. I'll beat your ass.... No seriously I'm not gay! Just don't tell anyone." I turn
back at him and say, "Don't tell anyone what? Nothing happened." I said it with a smile, hoping he knows his secret is safe with me. He blows me a kiss and drives off. I walk into my trailer and see that it's still empty. I immediately shower because the last hour of my life was totally unexpected, and I need to wash that nasty sex off of me. Once I'm showered and ready for bed, I make sure to eat my tacos so I can go to sleep nice and full.

I lay on my couch and think of how the curiosity of men excites me. Men will always be attracted to what they shouldn't have. I'm their forbidden fruit. I think of all the men in my school who have either tried to or have done something sexual with me. Soccer players, baseball players, swimmers, wrestlers, artists, band kids, engineering kids, freshmen, sophomore, juniors and seniors. Men from every aspect of our school. It's not only our school. Matt is not only a good fuck but the perfect example because he doesn't even go to our school. We have about 6 neighboring high schools and there's a straight guy in every school that wants me. Now there's two in Matt's school. As I think about all the men that want me, I keep thinking how not one of them compares to X. I just got fucked and I should be relieved but all I can think of is how I'm not spending Valentine's Day with him.

I actually feel like I cheated on him. Omg did I cheat on X? I toss and turn, trying to convince myself that it's not cheating, but I feel like I betrayed him. I should've spent Valentine's Day with him, he actually loves me not her. None of this is fair to me or her. I put my phone to charge when I get a message. "I know you're hurt and I'm sorry I keep messing things up, but I wish I was with you today. I love you baby, good night, dream of me the way I'll dream of you. – X" I read it and tears immediately start streaming down my face. I don't understand why these gestures cause me so much joy and pain at the same time. Why do all the things he says make me feel so special and worthless? I deserve better than this and I know it.

I think for a few minutes before I write back, "I had an amazing Valentine's Day. Don't worry, you're where you choose to be. Don't write to me again. Goodbye." He calls me right away, but I ignore it. He tries four more times until I turn my phone on Airplane mode. Not talking to X really hurts me, but at the moment I don't feel anything. I am numb to

everything. I might feel a little good that I'm not the one going to sleep tonight crushed. I set my alarm and attempt to go to sleep with the little
speck of pride I have left. Happy fucking Valentine's Day.

Chapter 6

The next morning, as I ride the bus to school, I can't stop wondering if I made the right decision. I still have my phone on Airplane mode because I'm not in the mood to see what X has to say. Knowing him, he's been blowing me up since last night and I don't want to hear all the same empty promises he always gives me. I walk into school and immediately see Ashley, who's more than ready to tell me about her date. "Glend!!!!!" she screams as she runs up to me and hugs me. "Good morning to you too Ashley." I can barely talk from how hard she's squeezing me. She lets me go and says, "Glend, it was amazing! I think I'm in love. It was just like a movie! He took me to the beach, and we listened to music all night. We went at like midnight, so the moon was bright as hell. We didn't even have sex! He didn't initiate anything at all. We already made plans to hang out this Saturday!
We're keeping it lowkey, so he doesn't want me telling anyone who he is. I want to tell you, but I can't just yet." She's smiling from ear to ear. I can't help but be happy for her. Even though I had a shitty Valentine's Day, that doesn't mean I can't be happy for someone else. "That does sound cute Ashley. I wouldn't know how to contain my excitement if someone did that for me. And bro, take your time! Have fun with him while you guys get to know each other. I'll meet him when the time is right." I say with a big smile.

The bell rings and everyone around us starts walking to

class. Me and Ashley don't have class together until later, but she will probably tell me more about her guy. Maybe I know who he is.

"See you at lunch?" she asks. "Definitely!" I say as we part ways. Four classes later, Ashley and I reunite at our usual lunch table. "Today's going by really fast, I blinked and its lunch. I wish everyday was like this." Ashley says. Of course her day is going by fast, she's on cloud nine. Everything goes by faster when you're happy but when you're depressed? A class can feel like ten hours. "I actually think it's going kind of slow but it's almost over so whatever." I say, trying not to kill the mood by accident. Out of nowhere, we see Britney walking up to our table. Ashley and I are both really confused because she never sits with us, but she looks like she's headed right towards us. Ugh I hate this. She's the last person I want to see. She sits and has a huge smile on her face. I know X gave her the reason; he makes me smile like that too. She was definitely looking for us because she looks way too excited right now. "Guys, I ended up finding the perfect dress for last night, no thanks to you two! Haha." She sarcastically whips at us. "We don't have as good of taste as you do boo, maybe we would've set you back?" Ashley says with a bigger sarcastic smile. "Oh, for sure, I'm glad everything worked out. Anyways, are you guys going to the party on Friday? Everyone's going." I don't even know what party she's talking about. Just as I was about to say no, Ashley responds and it's not what I want to hear.

"Yeah, we are actually going. I guess we'll see you there?" They smile at each other, and Britney says, "I guess so? See ya!" She gets up from the table and walks to another group of kids who probably don't want her there either. Better them than us though.

I turn to Ashley and say, "I didn't know anything about a party, did you?" Ashley nods her head. "Yeah, I knew, and I decided we're going. I'm not taking no for an answer. I promised I wouldn't say anything, but I found something out last night. Fuck that bitch. I can't stand her. I was trying to forget, but once I saw her, I immediately got mad." She says. I've never really seen Ashley this annoyed. Omg she didn't hate Britney this much yesterday. I did, but I couldn't tell her that. "Why? Has Britney done something to you?" I ask, with a tone full of curiosity. "She's never done shit to me, but I caught her cheating on her boyfriend last night, and I told you he's a family friend." She says, not realizing what she really just told me. I'm in complete shock, Britney is cheating on X?! I have to play it cool, but Britney cheating, could change everything back to normal for us. "This is really juicy chisme, tell me everything!" I say with a smile. "When my date was dropping me off last night, he gets a call from Kevin." She says. "Wait, which Kevin?" I ask. "The senior soccer player." I make a face. "Corny right? Anyways, my date puts the call on speaker and Kevin starts explaining how he took
Britney to get a dress for Valentine's Day and he fucked her."

I gasp "Oh my God." Ashley isn't done. "Once she got home from the date, she called Kevin over, and they fucked again. Kevin was laughing, calling her man a dork. It got me so angry, and my date noticed. He told Kevin he'll call him later and apologized to me. He begged me not to say anything, so I won't to avoid issues, but I can't hide how much I dislike her." My mouth dropped.

I have to contain myself, because I'm ready to overreact. "How could you not mention this earlier?!" I ask, almost as if she should know that anything that has to do with X, should always come first. "Honestly, I forgot until I saw her. I should tell my cousin, but he is the type of guy who will only listen if I have proof, and I don't. But with Kevin's big mouth, the truth will come out sooner than later." She says, as the security guards begin signaling that lunch is over. "Promise you won't tell anyone?
Also, tell your parents you're staying the weekend at my house. At least Friday night, we need to go to this party. We're not missing it!" I look at her and say, "I won't tell anyone, I promise! I'll tell my mom about this weekend, I'm sure she'll say yes." I get up and walk with Ashley to class. I can't handle this. I need some privacy. My mind is racing. Why do I have anxiety like I'm the one getting cheated on? I need some time to think. I don't feel good. "Ashley, I'm going to use the bathroom. I'll meet you in class." I say, as I break away from her in the crowd. "Ok, see ya!" she says. I go into the bathroom and find an empty stall to sit in.

I think I'm having an anxiety attack.

My stomach is in knots. I cannot believe what I just found out. I might throw up with all this. Britney did what? You sneaky bitch, you're cheating on X and making him a joke? I hate her even more now. Should I tell him? Yes, you love him. No, that would betray Ashley's trust. Yes, he deserves to know. No, he's doing the same thing.

What do I do with this information? I should've never asked, because now, I know way too much, and I can't handle it.
I check my phone and realize that it's still on airplane mode. I turn Airplane mode off, and the messages from X start pouring in. Apology after apology, I love, need and want you messages. Plus, a bunch of songs and shows that remind him of me. My phone has been on airplane mode since last night and he's the only person who's written to me. Not even my mom has texted me.
The last message says, "Meet me in the cereal aisle after school if you really love me. I'll be there waiting." Great now he's gaslighting me. I was angry at him an hour ago, and now, all I can do is feel bad for him. He's the butt of a joke.
Everything I told myself just flew out the window and I reply, "See you at the cereal aisle after school." Ugh I love him so much.
Later after school, I'm standing in front of the supermarket, confused as ever. Am I really standing here, where he wanted

me to, when he told me to? I probably wouldn't have shown up if I didn't feel bad for him, but whatever. Once the final bell rang, I flew over here. I didn't even say bye to Ashley. I'm hesitant to go in, but I also really want to. It's the biggest internal battle ever. I want to see X, I want to hear what he has to say, but I also want him to respect me and my feelings. I'm giving in too easily. As I stand there, a mother and son walk out. The mom is
asking how her son's day went.
"I'm glad you had a good day my love, I got your favorite ice cream. We can have it after dinner, just don't tell your father." She says.

"Oh my god!! Thanks mom, I love you!" he screams back with excitement. "I love you more baby." That was such a beautiful moment to witness. I felt the envy coil up inside of me. I wish my mom bought my favorite ice cream, she probably would, until James notices it's my favorite & then she would
never buy it again. That's when it hit me like a bag of bricks. X is really the only person who's checked up on me since last night.
X is the only person who cares what happens to me, and if I'm okay. Is that sad, or beautiful?
I take a deep breath and walk to the cereal aisle. No reason to waste any more time. I get to the aisle, and I see him standing in the middle, just waiting for me. He looks so handsome.
I walk up to him, trying to act like I'm still done with him.

"Why did you ask me to come here?" He looks to the right and points at a cereal with a rabbit on it.
"You know the phrase down the rabbit hole?" he asks.
"Yeah." I respond. I know this isn't what this boy wanted to talk about. I will walk away right now.
"Well, if you go down the rabbit hole, it's your choice. No one forces you to do anything. If you decide to go down, you can't get mad halfway down. It doesn't make sense; it was your choice." He says. I pause, think real hard, and say, "If this is your way of proving a point, this was stupid and corny. I can't control when you do something stupid that hurts me or makes me mad. If
I could control that, I wouldn't have a problem halfway through the 'rabbit hole'." He looks at me and starts laughing.

"I know this is going to get you mad, but I love your response. You responded exactly how I thought you would.
Everyone else I've told this to has told me they'd blindly follow me. You're different and that's why I'm in love with you." IN LOVE WITH ME!? YOU LET BRITNEY SUCK ON YOUR NECK! He's so cute though, that was a good setup. "Can you come to my house please? We need to talk." He looks so sad and hurt. I can tell he's been thinking about this a lot. As much as I shouldn't, I say, "yeah sure let's go."
Before we reach the exit, I look at him and say "Just to make something clear, this isn't me blindly following you. I'm going

because I want to." He smiles and says "I know. That's what makes it mean more."
We get into his car, and I ask, "Aren't you scared someone's going to see us?" He looks at me and rolls his eyes. He starts the car, puts on a song, and reverses in complete silence.
Two minutes pass, he lowers the music and says, "It's no one's business why you're in my car. If I want you in my car, I don't have to explain anything to anyone." Clearly, I struck a nerve. While he drives to his house we sit in silence. I'm confused why we're going to his house, but I don't even need to ask questions. It's like he can read my mind. "My parents are gone until Monday, so I have the house all to myself. I want to show you something."
He says answering the question I never asked. "Show me what?" He just smiles.
"You'll see." He says. We reach his house, and he opens the car door for me. "Right this way beautiful." He flirts. If I wasn't still mad at him, he would be getting head as soon as he walks inside.

As we enter his house, I'm mesmerized with how beautiful it is. Elegant furniture, family pictures, huge tv with a surround sound system. This is the house of my dreams. X has such a beautiful family. This is really everything I've always wanted. "Okay, close your eyes." he says. I close them and he leads me. "Wow, I'm really following you blindly." I joke, and we both begin to laugh. We walk a few steps, and he tells me to open my eyes. Once I open them, I see a dining table set up. "This is the valentine's day date I owe you." He says. It's a table set for two, there's two Mexican food bowls, soda, candles, flowers, and a bottle of wine in a cooler. I'm in complete shock, I wasn't expecting this. "You really did this for me?" I ask.

"Of course, I felt terrible yesterday. I just wanted to be with you. I love you." He says as he pulls me closer. "I love you more, let's eat babe." I say, as we walk towards the table. We sit down and begin having our valentine's date. We sit, eat, laugh, and just enjoy ourselves. One thing about X and I, when we talk, it's for hours and hours. Dreams, goals, expectations. We talked about it all. I tell him about the romantic comedies I saw last night, and he even told me that our story should be a movie. I asked why his parents are out of town and he told me they travel like that a lot.

In fact, he's more surprised when they're here. After an hour we finished dinner, dessert and now we're having a glass of wine "How did you know I was going to come?" I ask him, starting to feel the buzz. This wine is giving me the boost I needed.

"Honestly, I wouldn't expect anyone to come, but you're different. I know I hurt you, but I've never had someone love me the way you do.

Once I realized you didn't want to speak to me, my entire world crashed. I need to talk to you." I can't even say anything, all I can do is listen. "Matter of fact, I don't think I love anyone the way I love you." He says, as he reaches for my hand. Every thought has left my mind, I forgot why I was mad. The wine isn't helping either, I lied. My brain is only processing the beauty of this moment, nothing else exists. I chug my wine, get up, walk over to him and sit on his lap. "I love you more baby." I say, smiling. We start kissing genuinely with the passion of a blazing fire.

Probably, our most passionate kiss thus far. "Let's go to my room babe, I want to make love to you." He says, as he leads me to his room.

As soon as we're in his room, he starts unbuckling my pants and kissing me. He gets me completely naked, and then he begins undressing himself. For a moment, I'm in heaven. He's on top of me just kissing me. We're completely naked, I feel every bit of him pressed against. He's harder than he's ever been. He must've really missed me. He flips me over and says, "I don't even want head, I just want to be inside of you." He puts on some lube and starts putting his dick in my tight hole. With every stroke, I feel our souls connecting. He's holding my hands, kissing my neck, as his strokes become more aggressive. I don't even feel pain, I just feel pure happiness. "I love you so much. Say you're mine." He whispers in my ear. "I'm yours, I love you more baby." Once he hears me say that, he goes even faster. After about ten more minutes of love making, he cums inside of me.

Today, X and I became one. That dick owns my soul.

Once he came, he just laid on me. "Fuck, that was amazing. You okay babe?" he asks. "Yeah babe, I'm fine. Can I shower?" I ask."Yeah, let's shower." He says. OMG my first shower with

my man! It is just as intimate as I imagined. He's scrubbing my back and washing my hair. Nobody has ever done
me please.
this for me. "I'm so in love with you, don't ever leave
I need you." I look him in the eyes and say, "I'm not going anywhere. I love you so much" I dry myself in his room, and just think of the roller coaster that's happened today.
This morning I wasn't ever going to talk to X again,
and now I'm in his towel on his bed. I think to myself, about how I should learn to control my emotions and not let so many things get in the way of me and X. Being angry on Valentine's Day seems stupid now, I was the one who decided not to speak to him.
As soon as I'm about to put my boxers on, X barges into the room.
"Glend, hurry up and put your clothes on, Britney's
here!" That's when I begin to hear her. She's knocking on his window.
"Babe, I know you're here. Your car is here!! Open the
door, babe!!!" Luckily the window has curtains so she can't see inside. X and I look at each in complete disbelief. Aw shit, now what do we do?! I don't care but I know he must be going crazy right now. I start putting on my clothes as X begins panicking.

"Calm down, calm down. Just call her and tell her you

fought with your parents and you're not in the mood to talk. Tell her you'll see her later." I say, as I put my pants on. "You think that'll work?" he asks. "Obviously, why would I suggest something I thought wouldn't work." Confused boys are so annoying when they are scared of getting caught. He finds his phone and gives her a call.

He starts walking around his house while talking but as soon as I hear, "Thank you for understanding babe, I'll see you later tonight." I knew we were safe, for now. I hear her get in somebody's car and leave.

He comes in the room and says, "We're in the clear, she left!" with a smile. We both looked at each other and just started laughing.

"Bro, I can't believe that just happened." I say as I cry from laughter.

He comes up to me, gives me a kiss and says, "Thanks for always having my back, I love you."

At that moment, I remember Britney's cheating on X, and I'm filled with guilt. I can't believe I didn't remember this entire time. How am I supposed to keep this secret while I'm looking at him? I was having so much fun with him. The fact he's the joke of Kevin's friends just slipped my mind. "I love you too, can you take me home? I'm tired." I say. "Yeah of course, are you okay?" He asks. "Yeah, I just want to go home." I reply. His parents are gone. I could spend more time with him, but the guilt of what I know, is killing me. I can't do it. This is some sick joke the universe is playing on me.

Chapter 7

The next day at lunch, I'm sitting at myusual table. X and I are texting normally, and he told me that once he dropped me off, he chilled at his house for a few more hours and then he hung out with Britney. He said she was perfectly fine and wasn't suspicious at all. He made up some story about his parents, and she tried comforting him about it. She didn't even spend the night, she went home after an hour. I look around for Ashley but can't see her.

I text her asking her where she's at and she responds with "Taking care of something, I'll be right there." I finished reading the text and Britney is sitting right in front of me.

"Hey Glend. We need to talk." She says. What could Britney possibly have to talk about with me?

I look at her and say, "About?"

She takes a long pause and finally says, "We need to talk about why you were at my boyfriend's house yesterday. Care to explain?" Shit, I know this isn't happening right now. What the fuck do I do? Think Glend, think, use your brain!

"You saw me leaving his house?" I ask. She nods with a stern look.

"I don't understand why you were there or why he would lie? Why didn't he open the door? Why did he need to make up that story about his parents?" I must look like I've seen a ghost. I stay silent while she continues talking. "There has to be a certain reason why he didn't want me to know. I didn't want to ask him, so I'm asking you and I'm going to ask you one more time. Why were you at my boyfriend's house yesterday?"

Fuck. Now what the fuck am I supposed to say that? Let's see if this works.. "I was helping him with school. I'm tutoring him and he made me promise not to tell anyone because he was so embarrassed." Britney's body language loosens up and it seems like she's officially calmed down. She honestly looks relieved, maybe she has her suspicions about him. "Oh my god, that makes so much sense. I don't know what I was thinking, but I should've thought of that. Honestly, I'm such an idiot sometimes. My poor baby is getting tutored." She says basically talking to herself.

"Glend, thank you so much. I'm sorry I came at you like that, I was just confused. I was parked in the corner waiting for him to come out like a psycho. I promise I won't tell him anything about you telling me." Britney says, as she starts getting up.

"Help him Glend, he must really need it if he's asking for it. See you tonight!" She says.

"Don't worry, I'll help him! See you tonight!" I say with a smile. She smiles back and leaves. I sit in complete shock because, how is she just going to drop a bomb like that? You waited in the corner? Are you serious? How much of a self-aware psycho is this girl? She stalked the boyfriend she's cheating on. Also, where is she going to see me? Oh shit, I totally forgot today's that party. I just told her I was gonna see her without even knowing where.

Wow, maybe I'm the psycho.

I let out a little chuckle because shit like this only happens to me.
A few minutes later, Ashley finally comes to the table.
"Sorry I took so long, I was talking to my mom. You're still sleeping over tonight, right? My mom said you can. Do you want us to pick you up or can your mom drop you off?" She asks.

I hate moments like this because, I really feel embarrassed asking for a ride, but I know my mom can't do it. "Does your mom mind picking me up and dropping me off? My mom works really late and won't be able to" I say knowing it's a lie. "Yeah, of course! My mom will take you to get your stuff right after school. Will your mom mind? Omg, this is so exciting!" She says with a huge smile.
"No, she won't mind! I'm pretty excited too." I love that I am excited for this party. A little party here and there never hurt anyone. Plus, X and I are good so there's something to celebrate. I need a night of fun after the last few days. So much has happened, I almost forgot I fucked Matt on Valentine's day. As Ashley's mom drives to my house, I get a text from Monica. "Could you cover a shift tonight?" she asks.
"Can't, I'm sleeping at a friend's house but I can go tomorrow and Sunday!" I reply back to her. A few minutes pass by and Monica says, "Perfect, have fun. See you tomorrow at 3pm." I look up and show Ashley. "So, you're only going to sleepover tonight?" she asks.

"Yeah, I have to work tomorrow at three, but I'm ready to have fun tonight!" I say. "Don't have too much fun you two, you both have to be home by two. Ashley, you know I don't play!" Ashley's mom says.

"I know mom, we'll be home by two, I promise." Ashley's mom is your typical Hispanic mom. If anything, she's even cooler because she speaks fluent English and Spanish. She's super down to earth but I can tell she does not play. "Your mom said it was okay that you sleep over right, Glend?" she asks me.

"Yeah, I asked her and she's totally okay with it!" I respond, I didn't ask her, but she won't care. She probably wouldn't even know until the next day. We get to my house and I say, "I'll be right back!" I go in my trailer and see my mom cooking. "Mom, I'm sleeping over Ashley's tonight, I'll be back tomorrow because I have to work." I say as I start packing a bookbag. "Alright that's fine, have fun. Be safe. I love you." I finish packing and as I'm walking out I look at her and say, "bye mommy, I love you too." She blows me a kiss and I close the door.

Ashley lives in a beautiful house. It's one story but her mom has it decorated so nicely. She has a huge backyard with a pool. In total, it's Ashley's mom and dad, two little sisters and their dog Bubbly. I love coming here. Ashley always invites me to family parties, and the few times I've come, I always have a great time. They really treat me like family. "You guys hungry?" Ashley's mom asks. "Yeah, can you order pizza?" Ashley replies. "Yeah that sounds perfect, Ashley ask your sisters what topping they want." Ashley doesn't move a muscle. "Mom, just order two pepperoni and one cheese, they'll eat it. Come on Glend, put your bag in my room." Ashley says as she opens the door. When we get to her room, we see Bubbly in her bed ready to play. Ashley starts giving Bubbly kisses and playing with him. "Ready for tonight? I want to get fucked up." She says. "Isn't your mom going to get mad?" I ask. "She's going to be sleeping by the time we get home, trust me, I know my mom." For the next few hours, Ashley and I eat, watch a movie with her sisters, and play with bubbly before we get ready for this party.

I'm chilling in Ashley's room while she is doing her makeup, and her mom comes in. "Remember to be home by two Ashley! I will open a can of whoop ass on you." Ashley's mom says, with a half serious tone. "Mom, who the fuck even says that. I'll be home by two, just relax." Ashley says, as she finishes her make up. "And who's taking you guys?" she asks. Ashley turns around and says, "Mom, I literally told you this already. You met him, he's a nice guy and he's not going to drink so don't worry.

We'll be fine. You raised a good daughter." Her mom looks so happy. Ashley really does have a good bond with her mother. "Okay baby, you're right. Call me if you need me to pick you up." Ashley blows her mom a kiss as she's closing the door. "She's so annoying, sorry you had to see that." She says. "Don't worry about it. I think it's cute, she's overprotective." I say. I wish my mom cared where I was at two in the morning.

"Well yeah, she's my mom, that's what they do." She says.

Moments like this really hurt, because my mom didn't drill me this hard. I could be sleeping on the street right now, and my mom would be so hammered she wouldn't notice.

Before I let my envy ruin my night, I try to start a conversation.

"So who is taking us?" I ask.

"Well, I wanted to surprise you, but it's my date from Valentine's Day. I think I'm really going to take this guy seriously. Tomorrow we're supposed to go on a date, but I asked him if we can go to this party too and he said yeah. I forgot to tell him you're coming, but he won't mind. I can't wait to see the look on your face when you see him.

No one would've ever thought we'd be a thing." Ashley's phone starts ringing and she picks up. "Okay, I'm going now!" she says. "Let's go, Glend he's outside." We go to the living room to say bye to Ashley's mom.

"Guys, be safe! If he's too drunk, call me I'll pick you up. I love you guys, enjoy your night."

Ashley and I both say, "We love you too! Bye!" As we walk out and start heading to the car. As I get closer to the car, it looks a little familiar, but I don't know from where.

Ashley opens the passenger door and says, "Babe, this my friend, say hiiii" He gets out of the car excited until we both realize we know each other. I knew this car looked familiar, it's Matt's car!

We stare each other in silence. “Do you guys know each other?” Ashley asks to break the silence. Matt doesn’t talk but I say, “I think we do? I’ve gone to a few parties and seen him. Matt right?” I say as I extend my arm for a handshake. He doesn’t want to grab my hand at first but ultimately shakes it. “Babe, you’re acting weird” Ashley says. When he realizes how he’s acting, he immediately changes his attitude. He shakes my hand and gives me a hug. “Yeah, this is Glend! We go way back, been my homie for years!” Ashley looks at us a little confused before bouncing back to her normal attitude. “If I knew, I would’ve told you earlier, Glend. See babe, I kept my promise!” Ashley says all excited. “Ugh, I have to go back to get my lip gloss. Get in the car, I’ll be right back.” Matt and I get in the car to wait for Ashley.

“Please tell me you haven’t told her.” He says. “No, are you crazy?! Why would I tell her. I can’t believe you met up with her at the beach after you fucked me.” Before he can say anything, I keep rambling. “Also, you had a girlfriend. When did you start talking to Ashley? What the hell is going on?” We both keep looking at the door waiting for Ashley. “I didn’t know what to do alright. Just, look, you and I will talk, just please don’t tell her anything.” We see Ashley coming towards the car. “I won’t say anything you idiot, just play it cool.” I say back to him. He better act right, I love Ashely. I wouldn't do this to her intentionally. “I didn’t know which one to get, so I got both, which one do you like babe?” Ashley asks, as she gets into the car. “This one babe, gimmie a kiss.” He says. They start making out in front of me.

"Babe, that's enough. Let's go to the party." Ashley says in an annoyed voice. This car ride is so awkward, and Ashley doesn't
t 5 minutes
even notice. "How far is the party?" she asks. "Abou away, we're almost there babe." Matt says as he places his hand on Ashley's thigh. I'm in complete shock. This man uses the same trick on everyone. I look in the rear-view mirror, and I see him staring at me. Omg, stop. Shouldn't he be looking forward? Focus on the road dude. Wow, I can't believe I fucked Matt on the same night he went on a date with Ashley. This entire time Ashley has been talking about Matt when she was talking about Mr.Perfect.

All I can think of is, what if I told her the day after it happened. Her world would be destroyed. She said this guy was amazing. Yeah, amazingly curious. Matt finds parking right in front of the party.

"You guys ready?" Ashley asks. "Yeah babe, give me and Glend a minute to talk. Just bro stuff. Can't tell you haha." Matt says. "Whatever, don't make my friend feel weird. Hurry up, I'll be inside." Ashley says, as she gets out of the car. Once she's at a good distance, Matt turns around and says, "Look Glend, what happened between us was a onetime thing. It will never happen again. Please do not tell Ashley, promise me?" He looks like he's about to cry. Matt, don't worry, I won't say a word. I promise. It never happened remember?" I say with a reassuring smile. He smiles back and says, "Let's party then!" We both get out of the car and walk towards the house.

High school parties in Miami are exactly how they're portrayed in the movies. Beer pong, flip cup, unlimited alcohol and drugs, people fucking in the bathroom and bedrooms. I find Ashley in a corner talking to a few girls. I look around and see everyone having a fun time. Everyone is in their little cliques drinking. People are taking group pictures with each other while goofing around. These parties are big, because it's not only my high school that's here but some neighboring ones too. It's like a party of 5 high schools. I look around to see if I see Britney, or more importantly, X.

"What do you guys want to drink?" Matt asks. "

Surprise me. Glend, what do you want?" Ashley turns and asks me.

"I'll get a beer please and thank you" I say.

As Matt leaves, Ashley grabs me and says, "I can't believe you know Matt! If I knew earlier, I would've brought him up! Isn't he awesome?

He's so yummy." Trust me, I know he's yummy. I probably shouldn't say that though.

I smile and say, "Yeah, he's amazing! Bro, Valentine's Day was like 3 days ago. We have a long time to talk about him. No time lost!" I say, but instantly regret it. What the fuck, why did I say that? Ashley just looks so happy, who am I to ruin that? I have to make sure she never finds out.

Matt comes back with our drinks and says, "were you guys talking about me?" while chuckling nervously.
"No, we weren't, unless there's a reason we should be talking about you! Haha just kidding." Ashley says with an obnoxious laugh.
"No reason at all babe!" He says. I start sipping on my beer because I don't want to entertain this. As I sip my beer, X and Britney walk into the party. My heart immediately drops when I see him. They both look at us, but continue walking like they don't know us.

"Stupid bitch, I should slap the fuck out of her." Ashley says.
Hearing that throws me off, so I look at her and say "Guy, relax. Just let them be." Matt chugs his beer and says, "Yeah let them be, let's have some fun please babe!" Ashley looks at us and says, "Alright, let's party!" It's pretty packed inside but luckily the house is huge, and the backyard is being used too. Someone is
DJing and they're actually playing some good ass songs. Ashley and I are shaking our asses until we can't anymore.

A few shots, beers and games of flip cup later, Ashley grabs me and says, "let's go to the bathroom!" We look for the bathroom and see that the line is huge. "You think there's a bathroom upstairs?" she asks me. "Yeah probably, let's go check." I say as I grab her hand.

We go upstairs and can't find any bathroom. We go inside a master bedroom and see that there's a bathroom. "Look I'll go first while you keep guard and then we switch, deal?" Ashley suggests.

"Yeah perfect, hurry so we don't get caught!" I look around the room as Ashley uses the bathroom and notice how well kept it is.

The furniture is all dark brown, and it all matches. The bed is king sized and it's in front of a huge tv. There's a Mr. and Mrs. side for everything. The Mr. is definitely a businessman, because his closet is filled with suits, and the Mrs. has so many gowns and dresses. They both seem very elegant.

Ashley comes out and says, "hurry up and use it, let's go!" I rush

in the bathroom, and it's also divided into Mr. and Mrs., everything is symmetrical. Is this what marriage is like? The Mr.'s side of the sink has every cologne you can name while the Mrs.' has a perfume store on her side. They're totally goals. I pee really quickly and rush back to the room. When I step out, I see

Ashley wearing one of the Mrs.' gowns. "Ashley, what the fuck are you doing?" I ask, while I begin to panic. "This lady and I have the same body. I hope I'm still this size when I'm her age. Doesn't this dress look amazing?!" She says. I can tell by how carefree she's being that she's drunk.

"Ashley how did you even put this dress on this fast? I was gone for less than two minutes." I ask as I try to figure out how to unzip the dress. "Glend, don't be boring, try one of the suits on! I dare you." She turns around and says while smirking. "Also look what I found!!" She shows me a bottle of vodka. "Let's live Glend, come on!" I usually don't act too crazy but fuck it, I'm only young once right? I put on a suit and start taking shots. Ten minutes later, Ashley and I are five shots deep each, dancing in the middle of this room. We're having way too much fun; we even start jumping on the bed. "Let's start heading back, Matt must be looking for us." She says, as she starts unzipping her dress. "You're right, let's go." As I start getting undressed, I hear footsteps approaching "Fuck, Ashley. Someone's coming, I can hear them!" I say in a rush. "What the fuck do we do?" she asks, starting to panic herself. "Relax, go in the closet and I'll go under the bed." I say as we both start to hide quickly. Thirty seconds later, two sets of footsteps come in. I'm under the bed and I see that it's a boy and a girl.
"Do you think anyone's in here?" the girl asks. "Nah, I don't. We can talk here." The boy says. I recognize the girl, it's Britney but that's definitely not X.

"What do you want to talk about Kevin? I'm here with my boyfriend." Britney says. Oh shit, she's in here with Kevin. This bitch is crazy.
"Bro, you've been ignoring me all day. You already know how I feel about you bruh, I love you. When I see you with that dork I just want to smack him." He says to her. I have to hold in my

gasp, but wow, that's actually funny because Ashley wants to slap Britney so badly.

"Don't call him a dork. Look, I love you too, but you have to give me some time to figure this out. Have you told anyone about this?" She ask sounding more concerned about getting caught then hurting either of them. "Nah, I haven't told a soul." He says back to her. "Good, give me a few weeks and we'll both be happy I promise." She says. I don't know what's more shocking, what I'm hearing or the fact that Ashley hasn't jumped out of the closet and hit her. This little sneaky conversation of theirs is starting to feel like forever but it's only been a few minutes. I can tell Britney feels the same way because it sounds like she's ready to get out, but Kevin clearly has other plans.

"Can I have a kiss before you go?" Kevin asks. I can only see their feet but it sounds like they're kissing. "Let me fuck you real quick." Kevin says in between loud kisses. Wait, did he really just ask that? "How quick?" Britney asks. I'm looking at their feet, but I see Kevin's pants on his ankles, and it looks like he's already stroking. I definitely know they are fucking now because she's starting to moan. "Cum in me, cum in me." She says. I can tell he has her against the wall, a few more strokes and I hear him let out a long sigh, he must have come inside her. He picks his pants up and she says, "That's it for a long time, I'm serious Kevin!" He laughs and without hesitation, she begins to giggle, then they walk out of the room. Ashley and I wait about a minute before we both come out of hiding. We both look at each other with our mouths wide open. "Did you see what just happened?!" I ask. "Bro, I saw everything. I don't even know what to say. I'm in shock." Ashley says as she hands me my clothes.

"Let's change and go Ashley!." We put the suit and dress back and get out of the room. We make sure no one sees us go down the stairs and we rejoin the party. Matt's still in the same spot we left. "You guys took so long, what the hell happened in the bathroom?" Matt asks. Ashley and I look at each other and say "nothing!" as we each start pouring our own drink. Ashley and I are going to talk about it when we get to her house but for now it's just me and my thoughts again. I'm looking around for X and I see him dancing with Britney.

"She has no shame, look at her!" Ashley whispers in my ear. I guess we were both looking for the same thing.

"Yeah, but look at Kevin." I say. I catch Kevin staring at X the same way I stare at Britney. No one around him even notices that he's staring at something that's causing him pain. Seeing the one you love with someone else while keeping your composure is a pain I'm far too familiar with. I'd recognize that look anywhere. It takes one dumb ass to know another one.

"I thought Kevin was a douchebag, but it looks like he's hurting right?" Ashley asks me.

"Yeah, he's definitely hurting." I say, wishing I can tell her how I feel his pain right now too.

Ashley got too drunk to talk about anything after that. In fact, she fell asleep the entire car ride home. Once we got to her house, Matt turned around and asked me what we should do? I told him
that I'll carry her in her house, since her parents are asleep.

"Are you sure they're asleep?" he asks. "Yeah, all the lights are off. They're definitely asleep." I get out of the car and before I open her door, Matt meets me outside his car. "We need to talk about everything, please." He pleads. "Here's my number, just hit me up and we'll figure it out." I say, as I open the door, then I take Ashley out of the car and put her arm around me as I carry her into her room. I walk towards her door and look back at
Matt who's just staring at us like a sad puppy. I open her front door and was absolutely right, everyone's asleep. I walk her to her room and place her on her bed as quietly as possible. Bubbly woke up and even he knows not to bark. I place Ashley on the bed, take her heels and jewelry off and tuck her right into bed. I get myself ready for bed and lay right next to her. "Glend?" she says very faintly. "Yeah?" I respond. "I love you, tonight was great." She says as she turns around and goes back to sleep. "I love you too" I say with a smile. The guilt is killing me. I would never have hooked up with Matt if I knew Ashley was dating him.
What am I going to do?

Chapter 8

I wake up at noon and Ashley's still sleeping. I get up, shower and quickly get ready for work. Ashley's house seems empty so I'm just going to text her and let her know I'm leaving for work. As I write the message, Ashley's mom comes out of her room and asks, "Hey Glend, is your mom here?" "No, I have to catch the bus to work, she's already working so she can't take me." I say.

"That poor lady is always at work, here, I'll take you to your job. Let me get my wallet and keys, one sec." She says. My excuse for my mom never being able to pick me up makes it look like she's always working, but in reality, she's home right now. She's probably still drunk from last night. Even if she wasn't drinking, she has no car, and James would never pick me up. I hate that I have to lie, but I rather not say the truth. "Ashley isn't waking up any time soon. You guys got home before 2 right?" Ashley's mom asks as she walks me to her car. "Of course we did, she's probably tired from a long week at school." I say as I get in the car. "What time do you work today?" "I work at 3, but since I take the bus I like to be a few hours early just in case." I say, as I look out the window. "Yeah we're going to get there at like 1:30, you'll have some time to relax before work." She says. "Yeah, just me and my thoughts haha." I say, making a joke, hoping for this conversation to end.

The entire ride, all I can think of is how messy my entire situation is. If I thought venting to Ashley was hard before, it's ten times harder now. Also, her and I both saw Britney get fucked by Kevin, and we haven't even gotten a chance to fully talk about that situation either.

Ashley's mom is on the phone with a friend so thankfully, I don't have to make small talk. Should I tell Ashley about Matt? She seems to really like him. Granted, it's been a few days, but she still has a right to know. Should I tell X about Britney? Actually, what if Ashley tells him and says I saw it too. Would he get mad at me for not telling? Will he get mad at me for telling? I was drinking last night so controlling these thoughts were much easier. Now everything is coming at me at once. My mind is racing and I wish someone had the answers. I feel like my head is going to explode. I close my eyes and wish I was somewhere else. I envision I'm somewhere far away with X in a committed relationship. Our beautiful apartment with a wiener dog. A happy home. A peaceful life. Thinking of what we could have calms me down. Even if it's a fantasy, it's a wonderful place to be. I'm in a state of peace.
"We're here Glend." I hear from a distance. "GLEND, WAKE UP, WE'RE HERE." I hear again. I must have fallen asleep because I open my eyes and see Ashley's mom staring at me. "You fell asleep, but we're here!" I look around and see that I'm in her car and not in dream, I'm still in Miami Lakes in my messy situation. "Yeah, sorry, I guess I was still tired from last night, thank you again for the ride! I really appreciate it." I say

as I wipe the droll off my cheek and get out of the car.I begin to walk away from the car when Ashley's mom lowers the window and says, "I will always be here for you, Glend, anytime you need us, just call us. You're family! Have a great day at work!"

She drives off and I stare after her for a second. Honestly, that made me smile. It was exactly what I need to hear right now. She may not be my mom, but having some motherly love today really helped me change my attitude. I walk in the mall and decide to turn my phone off for the remainder of the day. I'm going to mentally check out and deal with everything tomorrow. I walk the mall, looking at all the stores until it's time for my shift. Walking in, my store is as busy as ever. I see Monica is helping a family pick out some graphic tees, but she still waves at me. I wave back and walk to the backroom of the store. I'm a few minutes early but that won't be a problem. I put my phone in my bag and stuff it in my locker. Company policy states that we can't have our phone on the sales floor, but everyone always has them anyway. I usually have my phone too, but today I want to turn it off and leave it in the locker. I make sure I look and smell appropriate before I work my shift. I'm not going to focus on any of my personal problems, just work all day.

I walk behind a register, clock in and say, "I can take the next guest!" and for the next few hours focused on work. Working retail on the weekends is the worst. Most people have the weekend off, so the mall is always filled on Saturday and Sunday afternoons. As a cashier who has to deal with returns and exchanges, I get rude customers all the time. Sometimes, customers get so mad at me, but I have to kindly remind them it's our policy. My shift was from 3 to close and I can't feel my feet but it's finally over. "Rough day Glend?" Monica asks, as she sees me closing the register out.

"Yeah my feet are killing me. I'm so tired, but I really needed it. It distracted me from all the issues I have going on. I didn't even take a break, so I have a little overtime too. I hope that's not a problem, I didn't notice until now." I say. I did notice but I don't care. I didn't want any time to think. "You didn't take lunch? Wow you must really be going through it. And the overtime is fine! You're never over hours so it won't be a problem. Just don't let it happen too often." Monica is such a "company guy" manager, but until now, I hadn't realized just how good of a person she is to the people that work under her. "Work is the best distraction and I'm not just saying that because I'm one of your supervisors," Monica says, as she lets out a chuckle. See what I mean. I finish closing my register and start organizing some clothes before my shift is truly over. For those who have never worked retail, just because the store is closed doesn't mean we're done. In fact, we don't leave until the store is perfectly clean. The closing team must make sure the store is up to standard because that's company policy. Plus, the morning team will bitch and snitch us out to our GM. As I organize a table, I can't help but think about how crazy last night was. I don't know what's worse, Me and Matt or Kevin and Britney. I guess her and I have a lot more in common besides X.

We're both whores for some good dick. Since there's no customers, it's hard to not think about everything but if there's one thing I'm going to do, it's laugh at my terrible situations. Once I finish my section, I get the green light from Monica to go home. I get my bag and start heading out.

"Bye Monica, see you tomorrow!" I say. "Bye Glend, hurry up or you'll miss your bus!" She says, and I instantly begin to panic. Shit! I totally forgot I have to take the bus home. I run out of the store hoping there's still a bus that can take me home. FUCK! I start rushing to the bus stop and see that all the buses have stopped running for the night. I instantly get annoyed because I never forget things like this. If I didn't have so much bullshit going on, I would've remembered to leave earlier. I guess I distracted myself so good, I forgot X doesn't take me home anymore. I go in my bag and turn my phone on with hopes of finding a ride. My phone has been off since I got to work and I have a bunch of messages from X, Ashley, Matt and my mom. I kind of feel loved right now, usually only X blows me up when my phone is off. The most recent message was from Matt and it said, "I need to talk to you asap, I don't care where you are, please answer. Can it be tonight?" The next message was from Ashley. One of her first messages was saying how we need to talk about what happened last night and her most recent one says "Matt canceled tonight. You think I did something?" My mom's message asked if I'm coming home tonight so I can let her borrow
Fifty dollars. Ugh. Finally, X's message said "Britney, Ashley, and you were all gone around the same time. Did something

happen?"

Four people asked me questions and not a single one asked me how I'm doing or how my day went or why the hell my phone is even off. Never mind, I don't feel the love. I can't help but feel frustrated and underappreciated, tears begin to stream down my face. On top of everything, I'm stranded at the mall with no ride home.

What the fuck? I sit down to cry and prepare myself for this huge walk I'm about to take home. Not only is it far but it's almost two in the morning. I stayed until everything was done, not just my stuff and now I regret it. Hopefully I can walk to a bus stop and just wait for the buses to start running again. As I calm myself down, I see Monica is calling me. It's probably to pick up a shift. She must not remember I'm only seventeen and there are laws we must unfortunately follow. "Hello?" I say, trying to contain the fact that I'm crying. "Glend, I know the buses stopped running. I totally forgot what time it was. You never close the store all the way down with the rest of us. Do you want a ride home? I can take you." She says. Wow, I really wasn't expecting that. Maybe somebody is listening to my prayers. "Honestly, I was just going to walk home. I don't want to trouble anyone." I say. "Shut up, if you're at the bus stop, just wait there. I'm getting in my car now." She says. "Thank you so much Monica, you have no idea how much this means to me." I say, with this refreshing sense of relief that comes over me. Not even five minutes pass and she's in front of me. "Get in loser, we're going home!" she laughs as she unlocks her door. I can't believe she gets that joke? I love her even more now. I quickly rush into her car and start expressing my gratitude. "Monica, thank you so much. Like, this means so much to me. Do you want gas money? Anything? You don't understand how ready I was to walk!" I say in one long breath.

"Yeah, your house is a little far but it's okay. I don't want gas money. I do want something though." Oh no, what could she want? "Okay?" I trail off, wondering what she wants. "I want you to tell me what's going on with you. I mean like, what's really going on with you?" she asks. Wow, I'm in complete shock. I rarely ever get asked what's going on with me. In fact, no one ever asks me how I feel. I think because I'm always happy and smiling people don't see the depression I live with. I'm going to be as honest as I can. I need to vent, but I'm scared. Gay boy problems aren't exactly casual conversation. "It's a lot, you don't want to hear all of that." I say honestly, still keeping my guard up.

"It's a long car ride and I want to know what's been going on with you.

Vent away. I know my cashiers, and you never miss a lunch break or keep your phone in your locker like you're supposed to. You also never forget to catch the bus." Omg she really does see me.

I'm hesitant at first, but I eventually tell Monica everything. I spend most of the car ride explaining all the messy details of my secret life. I told her about X, Britney, Kevin, Ashley, and Matt. From the very beginning to a few moments ago. I told Monica the ins and outs of my high school drama and the unique problems of an openly gay high school boy. “Wow, that’s a lot… I wasn’t expecting all of that.” She says, not sounding judgmental, but genuinely shocked. “Yeah and now, I don’t know what to do. No matter what I do, one of them will get hurt and two of those people mean everything to me. I’m damned if I do and damned if I don’t.” I say, feeling like I can breathe since Britney knocked on X’s door.

Monica’s the only person besides me that knows the whole truth, and I don’t feel so alone anymore. “Look Glend, do what makes you happy. Stop always pleasing other people. None of those people are sitting down worrying about your feelings. I’m not telling you to tell or not to tell, but do whatever makes you happy.” I just shake my head, listening to her give me advice I need to hear. Monica seems like she’s driving the long way and the speed limit just to continue our conversations.
“X seems like a liar and a manipulator. I’m sorry honey, but I don’t think he’s coming out any time soon, and Britney? She can’t keep her legs closed, and she’s letting this man cum in her at a party she’s attending with her boyfriend…. Trash. Ashley? She just started talking to him like a week ago, she’ll get over it.
You let her fall too deep in love, she may not. There’s a million guys for her to choose from. She’s still a baby.” Omg, she’s so right about Ashley, I should tell her before she falls in love. I can’t judge Britney though, I let a random boy cum in me because he touched my thigh on the right night.
“Matt? He’s either gay or bi but no straight man will have sex with a man. He should just live his truth. But honestly Glend,

fuck these people. Well.... You kinda already are but, not like that..." she says. We both look at each other and start laughing. "Yeah, you're right. Fuck them, who's worrying about me?" I say to her, feeling empowered and ready to conquer my problems.

We reach my trailer and Monica turns to me and says,
"Look Glend, you're a smart and hardworking kid. Don't settle for trash. You've been fighting and competing for X the whole time and, he's not worth it. Find someone that wants to be with you publicly and privately. Everyone deserves that. Have a good night." She says. "Thank you Monica, I needed to vent really badly. This isn't a conversation I could have with anybody." Monica looks sad, let me cheer her up. "I'm going to disconnect from them for a while and hopefully that's the right choice. I can't express how much I appreciate this conversation and the ride.
Have a good night as well!" I say, as I get out of the car.
As I walk towards the trailer, I tell myself that I'm
cutting X off. He's the root of all this. He's the beginning of my problems. I will no longer talk to him, and I have to stay serious about this. My mom and James are home, but I really want to take a hot shower before bed. They're both probably drunk so they
won't notice. I walk in my trailer and see that they're both asleep. I sneak into their room, take a quick hot shower and get ready for bed. I lay down on my couch and tell myself I'm going

to start doing things the way I want to. Fuck them, I'm putting myself first. My phone isn't close to me, but I can hear it vibrating. I ignore whoever it is and fall into a gentle slumber.

Thank you

Monica.

Chapter 9

It's Monday morning and I'm walking into school with high hopes. I spent all of Sunday rehearsing what to tell each person. I ignored everyone and made sure to not even look at my phone. I started with the easiest, my mom. She asked me for Fifty dollars, and I told her I didn't have it. I actually did have it, but I had to lie. I hate that I lied to her, but I need my money and she won't even pay me back. With the way James treats me I can't afford to be broke. Granted, I wasn't honest, but I did put myself first and that's what counts in my book. I'm making sure I'm okay in the end.

Hopefully I see Ashley before class, if not I'll talk to her during lunch. I'm not mad at her but I still want to see her asap while I'm feeling strong. I'm walking to class when I get a message from X.

"Can you meet me in my car before class? I need to talk to you." it says. I probably should get to class but I guess I can get X's speech out of the way. I was going to leave him last but fuck it, one less thing to worry about. I know he's going to be the hardest one but I'm ready.

"Yes of course, omw!" I text back. I'm walking to X's car full of confidence. I'm ending things with him once and for all. This is too much for both of us and I have to be the person to do it otherwise he's just going to string me along like Britney is doing to Kevin. I pass couples on my way to him and to be honest, Monica is right. I deserve public love, not just being hidden away like a dirty secret.

"Where's your car?" I text him as I reach the parking lot.
"Look in the back by the baseball field" he says. It's at the far-left corner, but I see him before his response.

I walk towards and remind myself out loud to be firm and stand my ground. This is the best option for both of us. He needs this to end just as bad as you so he can focus on himself and his girlfriend. The bell is ringing, so everyone is rushing to class while
I'm walking towards X's car. Everyone is so worried about getting to class, that they don't even notice me walking in the opposite direction. I finally make it to X's car, and he looks sad. Fuck. I get in the car and realize he's been crying."What's wrong?" I ask him even though I feel like I already know. He turns to me and the look in his eyes confirms my worst fear. "Ashley told me everything, how long were you going to keep Britney fucking Kevin from me? How could you do this to me? What am I supposed to do now?" Every bit of confidence I had, left my body. I'm being overpowered with guilt. Monica help! Fuck, I feel like shit now but there's no turning back now, the cat is out the bag. "Honestly, I didn't know how to tell you. It's a very complex situation. I was going to tell you soon, I was just trying to figure out how" I say. "SOON?! I thought you loved me and were always going to be there for me? What happened to that??" He asks, as he starts to get angry. Putting the blame on me like I told Britney to fuck
Kevin. This is bullshit. "I haven't even talked to Ashley about it.

Like I said, it's very complex. I didn't really know what to do. You're getting angry with the wrong person." I whip back at him.
ything. I thought she I didn't think Ashley was going to tell him an would've at least waited until she talked to me. She doesn't know she put me in a bad position, she doesn't know me and X love each other.

"I cannot believe she fucked this guy while I was right downstairs. She even let him cum in her. I'm so disgusted by her.
Oh my god, what a disgusting ass bitch!" He says, even though he does the same thing. Well, he cums in me, but still. Now this is when I start getting angry. "If you don't love her, why do you care?" I ask.
"Glend, now is not the time. Don't you see what this bitch did to me?" he asks. Oh hell no.Now I have to start raising my voice because he doesn't hear me, clearly. "You can't be serious?! You've been cheating on her with me this entire time. Also, you claim to not even care for this girl, so I don't see the issue. She cheated, who cares!?" I shout. We are both starting to get frustrated with one another. "Why are you making this about you?" he asks. "I'm not 'making' it about me, you made it about me." He goes to say something back but I stop him. "You're mad and hurt by someone you claim not to care about. You claim to love me and only me, so why do you care about who she's sleeping with? Who cares what she does as long as you get

to be with me…right?" I ask hoping this is the end of him crying over Britney.

He begins wiping his tears and says, "it's not that simple." Men will always say "it's not that simple" to things that are ridiculously simple. Nine out of ten times they don't want to do anything, or they want to do the exact opposite of what you ask, so they blame the complexity of the task. I pause for a while to gather my thoughts; I need him to understand me. We're already super late so I don't care about time, I want to say exactly how I feel.

"It is that simple. It's the simplest decision in the world. If you want to be with someone, be with that person and only that person. Be with that person indoors and outdoors. Be with that person day and night. Be with only that ONE person." X is just sitting there with that stupid look men put when they know they're wrong but won't admit it. "You want me to sit here and comfort you because your girlfriend is cheating on you? The boy who you supposedly love? You want to make me feel bad for not immediately telling you that I saw your girlfriend cheating? You went home with her that night right?" The longer he stays silent the more fed up I become.

"You're mad because you care about her. It hurts because you have feelings for her. You don't see how fucked up this entire situation is?" I say exploding on X. I've never been this angry with him. I hate him so much right now.

Tears begin to stream down his face, and he punches his steering wheel. The ultimate pity move, that guys do. I already said how I feel about this. Toxic. He's silent for a few minutes then turns to me and says, "You're right. I'm sorry. I was just angry and frustrated. I shouldn't have come at you the way I did. I don't love her, but I just feel disrespected. When Ashley told me you and her watched, I was hurt by you too because I felt betrayed. I realize now that I didn't even give you a chance to tell me." I like what I hear, but it's still not what I want to hear.

"I'm never considerate of your feelings and I'm sorry. Please don't be mad at me. I love you so much." Wow, that's it. That's what I wanted to hear. It's like he read my mind. After this conversation I don't know if I should tell him I want to end things
or forgive him and move on. He's distraught and can't stop crying. I know I'm not supposed to care about others feelings right now but it's who I am. I can't help but care. I don't like seeing my people hurt, especially X. I think I'll tell him in a few days. What matters is that I end things with him for my peace of mind, but it can wait a few more days. "It's ok, I forgive you. I love you too.
What are you going to do now?" I ask. "I know I'm going to break up with her before anything. Can you be here when I do it?" he asks me. OMG. I'm emotional support for my boyfriend

so that he can break up with his girlfriend. This is a joke. I know I'm supposed to want him to break up with her, but a part of me feels really bad for X. I know this really hurt him and as weird as it sounds, I want to help in any way I can. Even if that means being a shoulder for him to cry on because his girlfriend cheated on him.

"Yeah, of course. I'll be here for you." I say to him while grabbing his hand. "No matter what?" he asks. "No matter what." I say back to him. "Want to skip school and go to my house? My parents are at work." He asks. I know I probably shouldn't, but I really want to, fuck it. "Yeah sure, let's go." We're already super late, might as well skip the whole day. We drive off the parking lot and start heading towards his house. The car ride is silent, not even the radio is playing. I look at X and I know he has no idea what to do right now.

We catch every red light on the way to his house. By the fifth one, he finally says something. "Fuck these red lights. I'm about to run everyone over." I giggle a little and he lets out a laugh.

I'm happy he's smiling. We finally reach his house and X turns his car off and just sits there. I can see the pain in his face while we sit parked in his driveway. "I really fuck everything up. I almost lost you over such a stupid situation. I don't even know why I dated this stupid bitch when I have you." He says, with his head still down. My thoughts exactly, but why did it take her cheating on you for you to realize it? X is so stupid. "Yeah, I

don't know either but let's just go inside and relax. I don't want to think about all this negativity." I say, still feeling focused from f us sit Monica's conversation. We go inside his house and both o on opposite ends of his dining table. We sit in silence for 15 minutes before I ask, "So what are you going to do?"
He takes out his phone and says, "She didn't go to school today so I was thinking of just calling her and telling her someone told me about her and Kevin. I won't say who. She either admits or she doesn't, I don't care. I'm breaking up with her either way."
I can tell he's really hurt but I have no idea how to comfort him. Half of me is sad he's hurt but the other half is happy he's leaving her. I hate that I feel joy out of this, but I love X and want him all for myself.
"Just be quick and straight to the point. It's the easiest way." I say biasedly. I just don't want to hear them break up and make up in the same conversation. I move to the seat next to him and give him a kiss.

"I'm right here, I love you." I say. I need to remind him he has people that care and that's what really matters here. Even though this situation is weird, at least I get to comfort X. He kisses me back, takes a deep breath and calls Britney on speaker. The phone rings for a little before she finally picks up. "Hey what happened?" she asks. "Are you free? I need to talk to you." X says. "Yeah, I'm free, I just woke up. What's up?" X takes a deep breath and then says, "I know you cheated on me with

Kevin while we were at the party. Don't even bother lying because a few people told me they saw you guys leaving a room together. We're over." He says.
Britney is silent for a minute before she says, "Alright, bye." Then she hangs up. X and I are in complete shock. We look at each other with our mouths wide open.
"Did that just happen?" I ask him. I can't believe how cold she was about it. "Wow, what a bitch. Biggest regret of my life. All she said was alright bye? That's it? Fucking scum." X says.
He reaches over to give me a kiss and says, "Fuck that bitch, I'm never putting you through something like that again. Moving forward, it's just us two. Got it?" He then gives me a kiss. This isn't the best time to end things with X. Maybe I don't have to end things with X at all. Honestly, our problem is his girlfriend, but he doesn't have one anymore. So, everything's fixed right? No need to break up right now. I look at X and smile.
"Got it." I say with full confidence.
Over the next several weeks, life was perfect. I eventually talked to Ashley and Matt individually.

I swore to Matt that I'd never tell a soul, including Ashley. I reassured Ashley that she has nothing to worry about when it comes to Matt. Ashley also told me how she had to tell X about Brit but he swore he wouldn't say our names. Although Ashley didn't care about her name, she made sure to tell him not to ever say my name. Matt and Ashley eventually talked, went on a few more dates and became a couple. I don't even see Ashley anymore because she's always with Matt. I see Britney in the hallways, but she acts like she never even dated X. In fact, the morning after X broke up with her, she walked into school with a huge smile and walked right by him like she didn't even know him. She still hasn't started dating Kevin but I'm sure they still mess around. Once I got to work with Monica again, I updated her. I told her being with X is what makes me happy, and she was happy for me. She wishes she was there to hear the phone conversation with Britney just so she could laugh. I've been picking up extra shifts at work and trying to save for a car. My mom and James are the same but I'm barely home, so I haven't really seen them lately. I actually think part of my happiness comes from that.

X and I are still seeing each other. He's back to taking me to and from work. We fall asleep on the phone with each other almost every night. Whenever his parents go out of town, I stay over for the weekend at his house. He is all mine, and I am all his.

We make love every time we see each other. I can't get him off me and I can't stay away from him. We went on dates to the beach; we would go out to eat and we would go on long drives.

When we want to do something in public, we go 45 minutes north where no one recognizes us, and we get to have fun.

We've even started planning little vacations to escape from everyone. Now that I have his complete attention, he's become even more romantic than he was before. Every time he picks me up, he greets me with flowers and a soda. He tells me he loves me every chance he gets. We hold hands while he drives, and he opens the door for me every time. Everything was going in the right direction. My life is amazing. I am happy.

Chapter 10

It's April 2013 and the school year is starting the last quarter. "Good morning, everyone, and Happy Friday! Today's lesson is on…." Ms. Rodriguez says as she begins her lecture. I notice some words are still misspelled on the board but I'm still not going to correct her. "Pst. Glend!" I hear from the desk next to me. It's Ashley attempting to whisper. "What are you doing this weekend? I miss you. Hang out with me and Matt!" These last few weeks have flown by, I didn't even realize I haven't hung out with anyone besides X.

"I work tomorrow and Sunday but I'm bout doing something tonight if you are! Text me!" I whisper. Ashley and I used to have lunch together every day, but since she's studying for the SAT,

I've just been sitting by myself. I don't mind it though. I just spend my lunch eating and texting X. I still sit at our same table and luckily, no one sits with me. "I think I'm going to hang with Ashley tonight babe, she told me she misses me." I text to X. "That's fine babe, I'm gonna watch movies with my parents then.

Can we still hang out after school for a little?" He responds. Honestly, this X is amazing. He wants to see me every day, what more can I ask for?

"Of course, just pick me up at our usual spot. I love you." I text back.

Not even a minute passes and he writes. "Got it. I love you more." Ugh I love him. As I walk to class, I meet up with Ashley
and tell her I'm free tonight. "Oh my god, yay! Let's do something fun like mini golf!" she says. "That sounds like a lot of fun, let's do it." I say.
She lets out a huge sigh and says, "Ugh, times like this I wish you had a boyfriend so we could double date. Whatever, Matt and I won't make you feel like a third wheel I promise!"

Her comment really bothers me because I do have a boyfriend, no one can know though, so it's like it doesn't count.
I try to contain my annoyance and say, "Yeah, one day! I'm late for class so I'll see you tonight!" Lame excuse but, whatever.
The school day finishes and I'm waiting to get picked up by X. It's a few blocks away from the school but no one ever comes over here.
I usually text X when I'm here and he pulls up in 5 minutes. Ashley's comment has been burning in the back of my head. I have a boyfriend…right? I mean, X has never really asked me to be his boyfriend. Is he supposed to ask me? Would that mean we'd be public? Are we just friends that are in love? Nah, we can't be just friends, we just can't be! He calls me babe; he knows we're something too. I just don't know what that something is, and now that bothers me. I don't want to ruin our perfect bubble by bringing this up, but Ashley's comment has me curious. A few moments later X picks me up and we head to his house. "Hey babe how was school?" he asks.

"It was good, Ms. Rodriguez had like five misspelled words on the board so I'm wondering if she's doing it on purpose at this point. I just don't want to correct her because I don't want her to feel embarrassed." While X laughs, all I can think about is Ashley's comment.

"Ashley wants to go mini golfing tonight with Matt so I'm going to tag along." I say. "Yeah you told me you were hanging out with her, that's good babe. You should spend time with your friends." He says, as he drives to his house. "Yeah I'm excited, I don't think we've hung out since that party months ago. Her and I had too much fun."

I say. When we get to his house, he turns his car off and rushes to my door to open it. "I got it babe" he says. This is definitely boyfriend behavior, but I don't even know if I have a boyfriend. X and I are watching a show together, we promised each other that we can only watch it when we're together and so far we've kept that promise. "What episode was it babe?" I ask. "Season 6, episode 11 babe!" He answers as he gets the snacks. We cuddle and watch an episode before we begin kissing. "Let's go to my room" he says. "Let's go" I say as he carries me to his room. He undresses me and then undresses himself. Sometimes I do all the work, sometimes it's just him but today it was both of us. He holds my hand with every thrust. Kisses my neck and says he loves me.

He fucks me hard and says I'm his. We make love for an hour before he cums in me. While I lay in his arms, I realize that I am hundred percent in love with this man. "Let's shower babe, it's almost five." He says. He kisses me a few more times before leading me to the shower.While we're in the shower, the sudden urge to ask him "what are we?" pops up. I feel like asking right now but I decide not to. I want to just savor the moment. I don't want to ruin what we have. We don't need labels. I'm happy with what we have and where we are. As we get dressed, we both notice his phone is ringing on the bed. He walks over and looks surprised. "What happened? Who is it?" I ask. He looks up and says it's Brit. We're both confused as fuck. "Why is Britney calling you?" I ask.

"I don't know, I haven't spoken to her since the break up. I swear."

He says. He doesn't really look like he's lying.

In fact, he looks just as confused as I do so that's refreshing but I'm still pissed she's calling my man. "Well, call her back and find out what she wants." I say. A few seconds pass by and he starts panicking.

"She just text me saying she's outside my house and needs to talk to me right now." He says. Are you serious? Not this again. Fuck.

"She says she sees me here. That she won't leave until I open. What do I do?" he asks.I think long and hard before I tell him, "Just find out what she wants. You have nothing to hide right?" I ask. "No, I swear!" he says. "Ok, just let her in and find out what she wants. I'll be hiding in your room." I say. He looks really frustrated which is confusing but says, “Alright fine, thank you babe. Just stay in here. Let me just see what she wants.” He walks out of his room and gets ready to let Britney in. He closed the bedroom door so I can’t hear anything. I do hear the main door open and some mumbling but nothing concrete. I don’t like this, I need to hear. I can’t be that mature. I carefully open his bedroom door to listen to what they’re talking about.

“What happened Brit? Why are you at my house right now?” Britney is silent for a while and then she says, “I was cheating on you during the end of our relationship because I was unhappy. It doesn’t justify it but it was my only way of coping. I don’t even talk to him anymore but that’s not why I’m here.” Omg is she lying? Does she want my man back? X immediately asks, “Then why are you here?” Yeah that’s right baby, then why are you here you stupid bitch? All I can think about is how she could’ve just called or texted him if she wanted to say sorry. I’m so annoyed right now. “I’m pregnant and the only person who could be the father is you.”

My mouth drops and my eyes open widely, I don’t know if I should cry in silence or scream in rage. She’s pregnant!? Pregnant!? Wait, how is she sure that X is the father and not Kevin? I know I heard him cum in her that night. “I thought it was Kevin but the dates don’t line up. I’m too far along, the only person nutting in me around that time was you.” Real classy bitch. “I haven’t decided if I’m going to keep it or not. but I just had to tell you in person, so you’re not kept out of the loop.” I know X cannot handle situations like this. He can barely handle our little drama. This might give him a stroke at seventeen.

“Bro, what? I don’t know what to say. I’m lost. I can’t have a kid with you, we’re barely grown.” He says. I knew it, he’s freaking the fuck out right now. “I know this is a lot for you to take in. I found out on Monday and swore it was Kevin’s. When they said how far along I was, I knew for a fact it was you. I want your opinion on my decision. It’s technically our baby.” She says. Wow, as I hear those words, my heart breaks. It’s taking everything in me to not jump out and fall to the floor screaming and crying. “Brit, I don’t think I’m ready to be a father just yet, but it’s not my body. I have to support whatever decision you make. My parents are going to want a DNA test though. I kind of told them why we broke up.” He says. “That’s fine, I’ll let you know what I decide to do. Thank you for being understanding and I think you’d make an amazing father.” She’s right but I do not want him having a baby with her. “I’m going to text you by Monday with what I decide to do. Don’t tell anyone until I tell you what my decision is.” She says as she gets ready to walk out. “Got it, let me know.”

He says while he opens the door for her. When I hear the door close I rush to sit on the bed before X comes into his room. “You heard that right?” he asks. Fuck I can’t even lie. “Yeah, now what?” I ask. “She’s going to let me know what she decides. This sounds fucked up, but I hope she decides to abort. My parents are going to kill me if she decides to keep it.” He says. I can’t judge his response, but this anger overcomes me as soon as he finishes speaking. “Are they the only ones you’re thinking about? What about, oh I don’t know, me?! How do you think I’m going to feel knowing you share a baby with Britney?”

This may not be the time for this conversation, he looks pissed. X takes a breathe before responding to me. "What the fuck!? No, don't make this about you. This has nothing to do with you. Stop" I can feel myself getting angrier."My boyfriend having a baby with his ex has nothing to do with me?" I can tell he's at his limit, but I don't care. I do not want him to have this baby. "First of all, I'm not your boyfriend…." And there it was. He said it. He told me what I never wanted to hear. My face changes the second those words come out of his mouth. I know he knows he messed up, because he stops talking as soon as he says it, then he tries to take it back. "Wait Glend, I didn't mean that…I'm just frustrated." He says, as he starts to calm down, but he went too far for me to just let it go.

"No, you're right. You're not my boyfriend so I shouldn't care. Have fun changing diapers." He may have calmed down but I'm still furious. I get my book bag and storm out of his house. "Come back and let me take you home." He shouts. I see him get his keys and start getting in his car.

As I'm walking home, he pulls up next to me, puts the window down and says, "Glend, please I didn't mean that. I'm sorry I was just frustrated. Can you please get in the car so I can take you home? Please?" He begins tearing up and I can't help but feel bad. I look at him and his face is full of tears, stress and heartache.

"Please get in the car, please." He says.

I feel horrible, I can't see him like that. It breaks my heart. He hurt my feelings, but he has so much on his plate right now I can't add on to it. "Sure, just don't talk to me in the car." I say, as I head over to the passenger seat. The car ride is silent for the first ten minutes until X finally says something. "Please don't be mad about what I said. It just slipped out, but you have to understand it feels like you're making this situation about you. It felt like you were being selfish." I turn to him and to his disbelief, agree with him.

"You're right, it is selfish, and I think I have a right to be selfish. It's my life. Not only am I not your boyfriend but I'm always being reminded of it. Britney is pregnant and there's a possibility she might keep it." He's just looking forward, driving with nothing to stay.

"I know you'll stay with her if she decides to keep the baby. So, where does that leave us? Where does that leave me?" I look down and I start crying. X remains silent as the tears pour down my face.

I don't see the same sympathy I show him when he's hurt. I can't stop telling him how I feel though. "We always have a few great weeks and then something happens. We always hit this wall. This whole situation is too much for me X." Am I about to leave him?

"Ever since I could remember, I've always wanted a normal life. I shouldn't have to share you with anyone. I understand some things are out of my control, but I can choose not to be around this."

He looks at me and says, “You’d leave me when I need you the most? There’s a possibility Britney will abort the baby, what then?” We finally reach my house, and he puts his car in park. “I used to think being your secret was worth it because, you make me so happy. Up until about an hour ago, I was the happiest I’ve ever been. I can’t help you get through this. If Britney aborts and you have no more ties to her, call me. Until then, figure it out on your own.” He puckers his lips with some stupid face and nods his head. “Alright bet, bye Glend.” I look at him and say, “Good luck” as I get out of the car. I barely close the door before he speeds off.

I don’t really want to go home just yet, so I decide to take a stroll around my neighbor to process everything that just happened.

As I pass the different trailers, I wonder what’s going to happen. I find it weird that Britney told X without a decision already made.

Why wouldn’t she tell him when she’s already sure instead of giving X a weekend full of anxiety? And I don’t believe that she was only cheating on X at the end of their relationship. Granted, X was cheating from the beginning, so I wouldn’t be surprised if she was too. She also was way too casual about it.

When a bomb like this drops, you don’t have much time to think or act calm. Now that I think about everything, something isn’t adding up. I look at my phone and wonder if I should call X to tell him all of this. Half of me wants to, but the other half wants to let him figure it out. I’m not his boyfriend right? I still can't believe he said that. I reach PH and decide I'm not going to tell him just yet. I'm going to see how things unfold before I get involved. I'm sure X will come up with the same questions as soon as he processes everything. I mean what's the worst that can happen? I don't care. I'm ready to minigolf with Ashley and Matt. A few hours later Ashley texts me that she's on the way and I'm really excited. I need to get out of here and clear my mind. "Where is it that you're going again, Glend?" James asks. At least he's making conversation. "I'm going to play mini golf, there's a fun course at the mall." I say back to him. I wish Ashley would hurry so we don't have to have this awkward small talk. My mom is in her room getting ready and he's in the living room watching tv. Since I sleep in the living room, I thought we had an unspoken rule that while I'm here, they'll be in the room. I'm sitting on my couch and he's sitting on a recliner that he just bought. He told me he better not catch me on his chair, or we'll have problems, the day it got delivered. He's such an asshole. James is drinking a beer while watching a show so I can already tell he's going to be ridiculously drunk tonight. Thank God I won't be here.

He takes a few more sips before he asks, "You got a girlfriend yet?" I hate this question because he knows I'm gay, he just loves hearing me say it. "No, I don't have a girlfriend. I'm gay James, we've gone over this before." I say with a bit of an attitude. I don't even like calling him my stepdad but that's what I got. He doesn't contribute anything for me. I can tell he

feels I'm what stands in the way of him and my mom living the perfect life together. "Don't get sassy with me princess. I was just asking. You know, pussy will solve that little attitude of yours. You have to learn to be a man." He says while popping open a new beer. I can already tell he's going to be aggressive tonight, so I better come back when he's sleeping. I'm just sitting here in silence, because I don't know how to respond to him when he gets like this. Usually when I don't respond, he'll leave me alone. "Got nothing to say huh? That's what I figured." He says then under his breath I hear him take one last shot. "Faggot." He whispers it loud enough that
I can hear him, but low enough that my mom couldn't. My stepdad really is the most homophobic man I've ever met. I can tell he hates me. I just want to graduate and get away from him.Ashley finally texts me that she's outside. "My friend just got here. I'll be back later. Bye mom, bye James!" I say as I get up from the couch. "Bye baby, have fun! See you later!" She says from the room. She starts playing music so I can tell she's starting to put makeup on. "See if you could stay at one of your friend's house tonight, it'll do us all a favor. Bye fag!" He says with a smirk. He speaks up because he knows my mom can't hear him over the music. I roll my eyes and head out. I get in the car and Ashley immediately turns around and lowers the music. "Are you going to tell him or do I?" she says to Matt. Oh no, Matt you weren't stupid enough to tell Ashley about us? God, I hope not.
"Bro, Matt invited Kevin and Britney tonight with us." She says as she nudges his head. Oh you're fucking kidding me right? Not this bitch. "I didn't invite them, I told Kevin what I was

doing tonight and he kind of invited himself. An hour later he texted me saying he's bringing Brit.
I told him Glend was coming so he probably didn't see a problem. He's just like that babe." He says as he tries to give Ashley a kiss. She kisses him back and says, "You don't mind do you Glend? We just have to be fake for one round of mini golf." She says. I wish I could tell her I'm basically being fake all the time but now isn't the moment for that conversation. "I don't mind at all, the more the merrier." I say with a sarcastic smile. "
Bet, let's head out then." Matt says. On our way to mini golf, Ashley texts me saying "I never told Matt what we saw at the party or that I ratted this nasty bitch out, so he thinks we're cool. Just don't say anything and act normal. I'm not going to let her ruin our night." Wow so you tell X the whole truth but not Matt? Why is that a common trait between all of us? Britney is the last person I want to see today. She's the whole reason X and I are fighting.
How can I clear my mind of my problems while hanging out with the root of it?

What is she doing with Kevin if she just told X she was pregnant a few hours ago? I knew something was up. Maybe this is my sign to investigate?
I write back "Don't worry Ashley, I won't say anything, and I won't ruin the night. I'm ready to have fun! I definitely need it." Matt can tell we're texting each other but he just turns the music higher to distract himself. I could investigate for X,

but I could also have a worry free, normal night with my friends. Even though Britney and Kevin aren't my friends, I could just enjoy their company instead of thinking about X. Trying to snoop and get info to report to X is allowing him to mess up my opportunity to be normal.

Britney didn't do anything to me, she did it to some boy who isn't even my boyfriend.

Chapter 11

We finally get to the mall, and I'm just excited to play some golf, nothing more. "Kevin says he parked a few isles down, and to meet him at his car." We walk to his car and see Kevin and
Britney in it doing something. "Let's go bro, we wanna play golf' Matt says. Kevin lowers the window and flashes a grin."We have a bottle, you guys wanna take some shots before we go inside?" All three of us look at each other and I say, "what's a few shots right?" before we all start laughing. We go into his car and take a few shots together. I notice Britney is drinking too, so I'm assuming she's not keeping the baby. I sit directly behind her, so I don't have to look at her while she drinks. I don't want her to see my disgust. I'm sure if everyone knew she was pregnant, they wouldn't be this calm. We pass the bottle for a few more rounds and then Kevin says, "Let's sneak the bottle inside."
Us three in the back look confused but Britney comes to the rescue and says, "Put it in this water bottle and I'll hide it." Kevin pours the water bottle to the top and gives it to Britney. She has a big purse, so she just stuffs it in there.

"Alright, let's fucking go!" she says. Think about the baby bitch, ugh.We all get out of the car and start heading towards the mall. Kevin and Britney walk ahead, holding hands while Matt, Ashley and I follow them. They've been drinking longer than us so you can tell they're drunk. Watching Britney nearly trip as she walks towards the mall makes me question if she's even pregnant. What if she was just lying to X? Or what if this is her way of coping with the pregnancy?

I have to stop myself, reminding myself that it's not my problem. Enjoy your night Glend, that's X's problem, not yours. "They're a little wasted, don't you think?" Ashley whispers to Matt and I. "Yeah, Kevin's good but let's keep an out for Brit." Matt says. "Great, now I have to babysit this bitch too? You so owe me!" Ashley says. I laugh a little too hard and they turn around. "I'm feeling it, I'm sorry." I say to Ashley and Matt. We finally get inside the golf course and each of us are excited to see who's going to win. As we play through the course, my mind completely forgets X. For the time being, I'm a normal teenager with my normal friends. Well normal Miami teenagers doing normal Miami teenager things.

As we're advancing through the course, Ashley loosens up a bit, and we start talking with Britney. We pass the water bottle around and keep taking shots. The closer we get to the end, the more fucked up we all get, especially Britney. Her shots are almost twice as big as anyone else's. She definitely drinking her feelings away right now. We reach the final hole and Britney can barely play.

"Come on babe, get it together. You're holding everyone up." Kevin says. You can tell he's getting annoyed by her. On the last few holes, she swings and can't even hit the ball. On her final swing, she loses balance and falls. "Ow, fuck" she says. We all rush to make sure she's alright and to get her up.

"Are you ok?!" Ashley asks, as she holds Britney up. Even though Ashley doesn't like Brit, she's still willing to go out of her way to help her. That's just the kind of person she is. I admire her a lot for that. "Yeah, I'm fine, I just need to go to the bathroom. Can anyone come with?" Britney says, barely standing on her own. "Damn babe, you're killing the vibe. Everyone wants to finish the game." Kevin says. He's not even holding her up or attempting to help. He's just standing in front of her annoyed. "I already went so I'll take her." I say. Wait, what? Why would I say that? Sometimes I need to think before I speak. I guess seeing
Ashley be a good person made me want to too. Or maybe I'm just drunk, but fuck it, I'll be nice.

"We'll just go to the family bathroom. I'll make sure she's ok." I continue to offer my help like an idiot.

"Alright, dale Glend, just meet us in the front." Kevin says. Britney regains her balance and starts walking on her own.

"Do you need any help getting to the bathroom Britney?" I ask.

"No, I can walk just come with me, I don't want to go alone." She says. As we both walk towards the bathroom, she looks fine. We reach the bathroom and I say, "I'll wait for you out here." Britney looks around and says, "Just come inside and hold my hair while I throw up.. please?" God damn it. Why the fuck do I have to do this right now? But how can someone even say no? The girl clearly needs some help.

“Alright fine, let’s go.” I say. We both go inside the family bathroom and lock the door.

These are usually used for families who have to change a baby or something, but I guess it also works when a drunk girl needs a gay boy to be her bathroom buddy. She kneels in front of the toilet and says “Glend hold my ha…..” She couldn’t even finish her sentence before throwing up. I go next to her and start holding her hair.
“God damn it, I’m so drunk fuck.” She says. She throws up a few more times as I hold her hair out of her face.
“Did throwing up make you feel better?” I ask. I’m rubbing her back and giving her some water that I bought earlier.
“Yeah, I’m just trying to forget stuff. I’m so fucked up, I don’t even know where I am. I blacked out as soon as I got here.” She says. I know Britney is really wasted right now so it’s the perfect time to ask her questions. She hasn’t thrown up in a minute, so I think she threw all the alcohol up and now she’s slowly coming back down to earth. Actually, damn, she can barely keep her head up, asking her questions right now would just be taking advantage of her. I just want to help X, but if I ask her, would I make things worse? I know I said I wouldn’t investigate but I can’t help myself.
I take a deep breath and ask, “what stuff are you trying to forget?” Here we go. She wipes her mouth and turns around to me and says, “I’m pregnant with Kevin’s baby and I don’t want to keep it so I’m trying to find money for an abortion. I’m

starting to get desperate. I was hoping drinking can kill the baby so I can just have a miscarriage. I have no idea what to do." I know this is good news for X, but Britney is crying while she's saying this, I don't know how to be happy about it. Even though she's lying to X, I feel so bad for her.

An abortion wouldn't really affect X financially. He can spend the money and it wouldn't ever phase him. Would it be wrong to let her go along with the lie? Britney on the other hand doesn't work, and everybody knows her parents won't pay for it, so she's stuck.

"Have you considered telling Kevin?" I ask. She starts crying even harder. "No, he's not going to be happy with me. I love Kevin so much and I just want us to be normal." She doesn't even know how she ruined my "normal" today. "These last few weeks have been perfect with him, I don't want to ruin it. I finally have the relationship I want. I don't know if you know what that's like but I'm so desperate to keep it perfect." This can't be real life.

It's like Britney read my mind. I know exactly what
that's like. In fact, the person who is always getting in the way of X and
I is her. Ever since they broke up I've had a magical time too.

So, her plan is to convince X that he's the father so he can pay for the abortion and then she can be with Kevin. I knew something was
is crying with boogers

fishy but damn, she's bold. There she running all down her face, but I can't help acknowledging how smart that is.
"We're not even that close. Glend, please don't tell anyone." I shake my head repeatedly. "I won't don't worry."
She continues her rant, I guess she's an emotional drunk or maybe she's emotional from being pregnant.
"When I see you, I see someone who gets hurt too. I'm pretty drunk right now, but I wouldn't have confided in you if I didn't think you were a good person. Promise me you won't tell anyone, please."

I stare at Britney as she's at her most vulnerable, and I feel like an asshole. Ugh why me!?
She just told me exactly what I needed to have X never talk to her again. She doesn't know how madly in love I am with X. I could tell him tomorrow, and he'll make sure not to say my name. That being said, Britney does say I'm a good person. She sees the good in me. She actually sees me. I don't want to ruin that. I don't want to ruin this for her. I love X, but right now, I feel for Brit. If I keep this secret, she has her abortion, and is out of our lives forever. She doesn't want to keep the baby, so what's the harm? What if I never heard this anyway? She would still do it.
Right?
"Don't worry Brit, I won't tell anyone. Your secret is safe with me, I promise. Come on, you're crying a lot. Let's get you cleaned up." I say. I help her up and take her to the sink.

She looks at herself in the mirror and says ,"Jesus, I look like a mess." She gets the paper towel and starts cleaning herself up. She drinks the rest of the water and we both walk out of the bathroom. Before we reach the front of the mini golf course, she grabs my arm and says, "Thank you Glend, I really needed to let someone know. I know exactly what to do now. I know my secret is in good hands." She gives me a kiss on the cheek and we both walk towards the front.

When we get back to Kevin, Matt and Ashley, they ask us why we took so long. Brit explains how she was throwing up and I was taking care of her. She feels fine now, but just wants to go home.

We say our goodbyes to Kevin and Brit and head to Matt's car.

"Yo she was fucked up, and now she's fine, that's crazy." Matt points out. "How much did she throw up?" Ashley asks me. "A lot, I'm surprised she's standing, but it seemed she let everything she needed out." I say with a chuckle. I honestly think

I'm just going to keep this to myself. If I play my cards right, Brit will be childless by next week. I keep enough boys' secrets; I can keep a girl's secret too. The drive to my house takes forever. Matt and Ashley talked amongst themselves, and I was in the back with my thoughts. Am I a bad person for wanting Brit to get an abortion just so I can have X? Why aren't I thinking how this will

Finding out the truth,

affect her? Instead, I'm hoping she does it. that she wants to abort it, but can't, has me torn. Do I want to keep the secret to help her or do I want to keep the secret so I can finally have X? Does that really make me a good person? Am I who she thinks I am?

On the other hand, she's lying to the love of my life and I'm still keeping her secret. I don't know what that makes me. Am I keeping the secret for my own selfish reasons or because I'm a good person that wants to help her? Does the motive really matter as long as I do what I think is right? I look up to Ashley and Matt as they jam out while holding hands. I look at Matt and realize, I'm keeping his secret too. I haven't told Ashley that he fucked me two hours before their first date. If I tell her, not only will it ruin their relationship, but I'd be outing Matt. Who am I to do that? I should consider his feelings, but who's considering my feelings?

I kept Matt's secret because I want Ashley to be happy, and I'll keep Britney's secret because I want to be happy. If no one will think of, or consider my happiness, then I'll do it.

"Glend!" Ashley screams. "Huh, yes what happened?!" I say, startled.

"We're outside your house dork, we've been saying your name for like a minute." I look out the window and realize we're right in front of my house. I got so deep in my thoughts I didn't even notice.

"Sorry, I zoned out. Tonight was fun guys, thank you so much!" I say.

Ashley turns around and says, "Glend, we love you. Next time, I'll make sure Brit and Kevin don't come! Have a good night, text me!" She's really sweet. "You guys are amazing, thank you again.

Dale, I'll text you." I say, and get out of the car.

I walk in the trailer and both my mom and stepdad are asleep. Thank God, I don't want to deal with a drunk aggressive James right now. I look at the clock and realize it's almost 2 in the morning. This is early for them, but I'm not complaining. I get ready for bed and before I go to sleep, I take pride, knowing I'm making the right decision. I'm doing what makes me happy. X and I just have to overcome this, and we'll finally be together. After

Britney is out of the picture, we're one step closer to being the public couple we deserve to be. I hope. I fall asleep thinking of us walking the hallways while holding hands. Dreaming of our beautiful life together, I can't help but smile as I fall into a deep slumber, filled with joy and happiness. X will be mine and I will be his. Soon everything will be back to the way it should be.

Chapter 12

I decided to give X some space for the weekend. Sure, I miss talking to him, but I'm content knowing once this abortion thing is over, we'll be together. It's a small sacrifice for the bigger picture. I worked Saturday and Sunday, so the days went quickly. I made sure not to talk to X so he can have all the time he needs to prepare. Before I knew it, it was Monday, and I was eating lunch. I sit at my usual table, but Ashley doesn't look like she's coming. I've kept an eye out for X, but I haven't seen him all day.

I look around and see Kevin with his teammates, but I don't see Britney anywhere either. She's usually around socializing, going to every table and saying hi. It's kind of strange that I haven't seen either of them. I wonder if they skipped school to get this abortion over with. The school day was over in a blink of an eye, and I still haven't seen X or Britney. Ashley and I walk out of school together and both agree the daytime is just flying. "Bro, I can't believe today went by that quickly. I feel like I just got here

20 minutes ago." She says, as we walk towards my bus stop. "Yeah same, honestly, Friday night felt like it happened last night.

That's how fast the entire weekend went by." I say. "Yeah, I agree.

Speaking of Friday, have you seen Brit today?" Ashley asks. "No,

I haven't, I usually see her at lunch, but she ghosted today." I say back. "Don't say anything, but after mini golf, her and Kevin got into a nasty fight. Kevin didn't want to tell Matt what they fought about, but he said it was really serious, and she acted completely crazy." She says.

Oh really? I wonder how their fight went, I kind of wish I was there to see it. I wonder if she told him she's pregnant and wants to get the abortion? I roll my eyes and say, "She was really drunk on Friday, the fight was probably stupid." Ashley puckers her lips and nods her head in agreement. "Did she say anything to you in the bathroom?"

What a random question, I wonder if she knows and she's fishing? I doubt it though, Ashley would tell me if she knew Britney is pregnant. Right? We reach the bus stop, I look at Ashley and say,

"No, she just threw up the entire time and I gave her water. She could barely talk." She looks disappointed. "Ugh, I thought she would've told you something juicy so I could piece everything together. I wonder if she's fucking with her ex again? That would be hilarious. I'd have to laugh in that idiot's face." I wish I could disagree but same.

"Nah, I doubt they're talking again. She was just with Kevin. She would literally have no shame." I say.

"That bitch doesn't care. Maybe he's the only one who would put up with her, because Kevin was in way over his head on Friday.
She wouldn't rebound the rebound with the original guy would she?" Ashley says still playing detective.
I wish I could tell her what's going on but it's better to just keep my mouth shut and let everything just happen.
say, hoping it ends
"That would be too messy, even for Britney." I the conversation.
"Yeah, you're right. I'm just overthinking it. I'm going to meet my mom at the pizza spot, I'll see you tomorrow. Love you Glend!" She says, as she crosses the street.

"Alright, I'll text you! Love you too!" I say while I wait for my ride. The bus arrives and I'm finally on my way home. That conversation with Ashley felt longer than the entire school day. There's no way X and Brit would get back together. There's no possible way, she doesn't even want X, she wants Kevin. Today she tells X she wants an abortion, he'll pay for it, and then they'll both go their separate ways. I'm sure of it. I won't even text X to make sure he has enough space so he can keep a clear mind. I'm sure everything will fall into place.
The following morning, I get to school bright and early.
I walk in the door with my head held high. Today's the day I talk to X and comfort him. Today is the day we start over. Today is day one of the rest of our lives. I look around for X, but don't see him. I walk into my first class, and I'm ready for the day to go by as quickly as yesterday. While I'm in class, I pay attention

and write notes. Basically, if I do what I'm supposed to do, the day goes by quicker. By the time I reach third period I feel the day moving quickly.

Before my next period, I have to go to the restroom. I'm not one to consistently ask for a bathroom pass, so teachers usually don't mind. I quickly sprint to the bathroom, piss, and start heading back to class. Before I turn the corner, I see Britney walking towards me. She waves from across the hall. "Glend, wait! I have to talk to you." She starts sprinting towards me. I wonder what she has to say. Probably to let me know her abortion plans.

Maybe she'll tell me what she fought with Kevin about? She finally catches up to me panting. "Oh my god, what an exercise haha. I literally can't breathe." She says while breathing heavily. "Relax Brit, catch your breath. Don't pass out on me haha. What's up?" I ask. "Well, remember the thing I told you on Friday?" she responds. I didn't think she'd honestly remember, she was hammered.

"Yeah, I do. What happened?" I ask. "Well, I needed money, so I hit up my ex." Omg exactly what I want to hear. I should get to class but this is way more important. I hope I don't look too thirsty for the info.

"So, what happened?" I ask. "I told him I was pregnant, and he said he would help me with anything I need. We met up on Saturday so he could give me the money and he took me to the abortion clinic. Since I'm under 18, we had to go to an abortion clinic that wouldn't ask my age. They gave me this pill that helped me miscarry. He spent every day with me until this morning." Wow, X is such a nice guy. He didn't have to do all that.

"He held my hand through everything. We talked a lot about our relationship, and where we felt like each of us went wrong. I apologized for cheating on him, and he said he's done his dirt too. I didn't bother asking because I don't want to know."

She says. Wait so now I'm dirt? Hold the fuck up. "Long story short,

I can't believe I ever thought I was in love with Kevin. Being with Kevin and seeing how he treated me made me realize who I truly love. Thank you for keeping my secret, I'm not pregnant anymore." Omg please stop, don't say it Britney I was just starting to like you.

"This weekend made me realize that I didn't appreciate

my ex and the kind of guy he is. He's the one I truly love. I know you have to go to class, but please don't tell anyone what I told you on Friday." This bitch. She's ranting and all I can think about is throwing up.

"I can't let anything get in my way. By the end of this week, I'll be with the man I'm supposed to be. Fuck, I've been rambling. I gotta get to class too, I'll see you around. Thank you Glend!"

She says, as she starts to sprint to class, leaving me stuck.

I stand in the same spot for about five minutes. My body is numb. I have such a mixture of emotions that I physically don't

know how to function. All I can do is breathe in, and out, and try to stay standing. I'm just in shock. Did this bitch… just tell me… that her and X are getting back together? I look around to make sure I'm awake and not in a nightmare. I want to throw myself off the second floor to make sure I'm not dreaming. This bitch really thinks she pulled a fast one. All I can think of is how I'm going to get back at this bitch. I will not lose X like this. Fuck her and her secret. I finally regain feeling in both my legs. I'm walking back to class and all I can think about is how Britney really fucked with the wrong one and she doesn't even know it. This bitch is about to have a rude awakening. If X is going to be with anyone
by the end of the week, it's going to be ME!
I get back to class and immediately text X, "Can you skip fourth period and meet me at your car?" A few minutes pass and he responds with, "Sure. See you there." My anger is through the roof as I wait patiently until the bell rings for the next period. I have to try not to spaz on him. The bell rings and I'm rushing to his car.

All I see is red. I don't see anything else but the hallway to get to the student parking lot. As I walk down the hall, someone pulls my arm. "Yo Glend!" They say. I turn around and see its Kevin. Let me calm down, I don't want him to notice how mad I am.
"Yo what's up?" I say as my vision clears, I notice his eyes are swollen from crying. "Ay bruh, did Brit tell you anything in the bathroom?" He asks me. I take a moment to gather my thoughts

and say, "No, she didn't, she just threw up the whole time we were there." I can see his eyes tearing up some more.

"I really loved that girl, but you know, I'm not playing these little
games anymore. This shit ain't love man, only an idiot would continue letting her play them. I love her, but I love me more." He says, as he wipes his tears. Omg did she already tell him she's getting back with X? "I'll find a girl who's really bout loving me.
Fuck these games. And Glend? If you're in some shit like this, drop it. If they gotta pick between you and another person, they're not worth." He says, while giving me a hug. What the fuck is going on? I can tell he's really sad, because we've never even interacted this much. He's never given me this much advice. "Thank you Kevin, you're absolutely right. I gotta take care of something. I'll talk to you later." I say, as I continue heading to
X's car. My entire mindset shifts with that conversation. Kevin is right, fuck both of them and their little games. Before I know it,
I'm reaching X's car and he's already in there. He usually parks in the corner so it's not like anyone will see us interacting.

I take a seat in his car, turn to him and say, "We're
done." I'm not even going to let him know I know that he's back with Britney or how he spent time with her. "You're really

done?" He asks, as he reaches for my hand. I quickly move it away from him and say, "Yes, I'm done. I know my worth, and I don't deserve this. We keep playing this game and my heart isn't a game. I don't want explanations or long paragraphs. Once I get out of this car, consider me dead. Got it?" The words leave my lips and I feel like I'm stabbing myself in the heart a million times.

I watch X, as tears begin to stream down his face.

X is in disbelief. I don't know what he was expecting out of this conversation or if I'm making it easier for him to be with Britney, but I don't care, Kevins words are ringing in my ear.

"If that's what you want, I can't stop you. I will always love you Glend, and you can always call me if you need me. I don't think you'll ever talk to me again and I deserve it. Maybe in the future, we can try again when things are different." Fuck you X. That's all I can think right now. I sincerely don't feel anything. I'm numb to all of this. I'm so used to the pain it feels normal at this point. I can't even cry with him. "Good bye, and take care." I say, as I get out of the car. X stays sitting with his head down. As I walk away I can hear him punching his steering wheel.

Newton's

Law never fails to amaze me. I'm walking back to the school, but I still don't feel any sadness. Kevin's right, I shouldn't have to fight for a spot, and he shouldn't either. Usually when X and I fight, my body is consumed with sadness. I usually feel the sadness overpower everything and take over, but right now, I just feel numb. I'm tired of this back and forth.

If this sad twisted story is my idea of love ,then maybe I'll wait to look for love in college because this can't be it. I walk into class a few minutes late but we have a substitute, so it doesn't matter. I sit at my desk while everyone interacts with each other, with my headphones in and arms crossed, processing the last hour of my life. Why is it that I always go through things like this? It would be awesome to vent to someone, but yet again, I only have myself. No one will ever understand me, and that's just the sad truth. Usually, I'd be crying by now, but I just sit in pure silence and numbness.

For the remainder of the week, I don't think I talked at all and what's worse is that no one even wondered why. It's Friday, I'm in the lunch line and not a single person has noticed that I haven't talked since Tuesday. At home, my mom and stepdad are too busy with their lives to notice me and I haven't had to work. No teacher has called on me and there haven't been any group projects. There hasn't been any reason for someone to go out of their way to talk to me, therefore, no one has. It's funny how your perspective on your life changes based off of your mood. My life has always been like this, and yet when I was with X, I was still as happy as ever. The only difference between this week and last week is that X and I aren't together. Nothing else has changed though. I'm still poor, I still come from an abusive household, I still go days without eating. Instead of worrying so much about X, I should be working hard to build a life for myself.

I grab my food and not even the lunch lady says anything to me. I walk towards my table and notice how no one else sits there.

All the other lunch tables are filled with kids and their friends and then there's this empty table. I sit down and get my phone, ready to watch a show. I haven't really seen Ashley all week, and she's usually the one who takes me out of this funk. She may not know what's going on in my life, but she always brings out the best in me.

I sit down and let out a sigh. I look up and see Britney and X are sitting together a few tables down. She's feeding him French fries while they both giggle. What a stupid view. What a stupid little boy. Right before I'm about to start eating, I feel a tap on my shoulder. I look to my left and it's Ashley.

"Hey stranger! Sorry I've been MIA, I've been really stressed with school but you're doing okay right?" I'm in complete disbelief. I struggle to say something since I haven't talked in days. I feel so sad.

"Yeah I'm fine, I've been stressed too." I say with a raspy voice.

"Glend, you sound terrible. Here…have some water for your throat." She hands me the water and I can't help but smile. Ashley always makes me feel good. "Anyways, I came to tell you to come to my house tonight! My family is throwing a party and I would love for you to come. You know how my family gets down!" Her family is the best, I love them just as much as I love her.

"If anything, my mom can ask your mom, you know she loves you. My mom and I will pick you up and drop you off later." She says. Wow, I'm so grateful for Ashley, she always knows what to say to cheer me up. Even though she has no idea how badly I'm struggling, she treats me in a way that brightens my day.

"I'm gonna text my mom but I'm pretty sure she's going to say yes! I'll rush home after work. What time do you want me to be ready?" I ask. "Just be ready by six thirty, the party starts at eight, but my mom has to set up and stuff. Unless your mom can take you, then come at eight!" I know my mom can't take me I'll be ready at six thirty. "I can't wait, I really need this escape from school and Matt. I have to update you on so much. I have to run back to help a teacher, but see you later!" She says as she races back into the school. I'm very blessed to have Ashley. I immediately feel the happiness taking over the numbness. I'm smiling, and I can't wait for tonight. I look over to Britney and X, but they've already left. I chuckle and start eating my food. Fuck them both, I'm going to have some fun tonight. I'll have a new guy looking for me soon.

I make sure I'm the first one at the bus stop after school. I want to go home as soon as possible! Having something to look forward to, changed my mood. I'm happy and excited! As soon as I get off the bus, I sprint to my house. I feel like a little kid, but

I

don't care. I walk in my trailer and my mom and stepdad are watching tv.

"Mom, I'm going to a party at Ashley's tonight! Is that okay?" I ask. She walks up to me and gives me a kiss on the forehead.

"Of course, just be safe please. I love you." She says to me. I can't help but feel loved after a rough week, but James will always be here to remind me of why I hate this trailer.

"Try to see if you can sleep over too, make it easier… okay?" My stepdad asks. "I don't think I'm sleeping over James, sorry, maybe next time?" I say with a sarcastic smirk. Fuck him. He rolls his eyes and continues watching tv. As I relax on my couch, I get a text from Ashley. "Hey! My mom can't get you. She's way too busy setting up. My family from Colombia came and she's hosting. Just tell your mom to drop you off at eight thirty! I can't wait to see you!" Ughhh, now I have to find a ride. My happy bubble is officially popped.
I can probably take the bus if I have to and then try to get a ride back. I am determined to have fun tonight. I am not giving up this easy.
"Talked to my mom, she'll drop me off at eight thirty! Can't wait to see you either!" A little before seven I begin getting ready. While my mom and stepdad are in the living room, I use their room to get ready. I love getting ready around this time because they're both sober, just watching tv, and it feels like this is my room, and my life feels normal. I leave my phone charging on my mom's bed while I'm in the shower. A nice warm shower does my skin so much justice. I wash my hair and make sure to scrub every inch of my body. I brush my teeth and put on some really nice cologne. I make sure to look extremely presentable.

My clothes are ironed, and my hair is gelled back. I don't want to make a bad impression on Ashley's extended family. I've met them a few times and they're so nice but still, I always try to dress to impress with the little I have!

Once I'm ready, I walk to my phone to check the time. It's a few minutes past seven thirty so I'm still early, but I noticed I have a missed call from Matt and a text asking, "Hey are you going to Ashley's tonight?" Now that I think about it, Ashley did say she needed an escape from him. I wonder if he's going tonight? I'm hesitant at first but I decide to call him back to see what's up. It doesn't even ring twice and he already answers. "Hello?" I ask. "Hey Glend, are you going to Ashley's tonight?" he asks. "Yeah I am, my mom is about to take me." I respond. "Fuck, do you think I could take you? I need to talk to you." He asks me. I wonder what he needs to talk to me about, and I really do need a ride. I might as well say yes.

"Yeah you can take me, how long until you can be here?" I ask.

"I'm down the street, I'll be there in five minutes." He says, as he hangs up.

Three minutes later, I get a "I'm outside." Text. Wow, that was fast! He must really need to talk to me. Maybe they broke up? I hope him giving me a ride doesn't get me in trouble with Ashley. I step out of my mom's room and say bye to her and my stepdad.

"Bye guys, I'll be back later!" I say getting ready to walk out of the door.
"Have fun and be careful, I love you!" my mom says.
"Yeah, yeah, have fun, try to see if you can stay over there!" My stepdad says following up behind her.

My mom turns to him and says, "Stop telling him that, if he doesn't want to sleep there he doesn't have to. He has a home." My stepdad looks at my mom full of anger and then quickly changes his tone.
"Yeah, you're right, have fun Glend!" I can tell they're about to bicker. I walk out and as I lock the door, I hear them somewhat arguing.
"Stop talking to Glend like that, you make him sound like a burden. Respect him!" My mom says. I walk away from the door a little worried it can get worse but they're sober so I'm sure they'll be fine.
I get in Matt's car and say "Hey Matt, what's up?" His legs are shaking so I can tell he's anxious.
"Hey Glend, we need to talk." He says, as he starts driving to Ashley's. I'm generally curious what could have made him so shaken up that he's so impatient to talk to me. I haven't told anyone about our secret.
"Okay, about what?" I ask.
"Have you noticed that Ashley has been MIA during lunch?" he asks.

"Yeah, I think she said something about helping a teacher." I say. He chuckles and asks, "You know who else has been MIA during lunch?" My mind is completely blank.

"No, I don't know. How do you know? You don't even go to our school." I say. "If you've placed close attention, you'll notice that Kevin hasn't been around either. They both would text me during lunch and I just find it coincidental that neither of them are texting me and nowhere to be found now." Now that I think of it, I haven't really seen Kevin since Tuesday. Matt might be right.

"I haven't seen Ashley all week and she barely responds to me. She didn't even invite me to this party. She said it was only family, but she invited you! I don't want to think the worst, but I have a hunch and I need you to find something out for me." I open

my eyes widely and ask, "Me!? Why me!?" Why is this kid sending me to be a spy? He can't be serious. Ashley is like my best friend. I would never do that to her. "Because she'd never expect it from you. Please Glend, I know you can keep a secret because you've kept ours. I swear I won't tell her you told me. If I confront her, I'll do it smoothly and keep you out of it." I know he's taking me to the party, but I'm about to just get out of the car. This is too crazy, and I can't do it, he might as well pull over now.

"Look Matt, Ashley is a good friend to me. I don't want

to be a spy, I'm tired of keeping secrets. If you're suspicious, just ask her directly. This has nothing to do with me, I'm sorry. If you don't want to take me to the party anymore, let me know, and I'll walk the rest of the way." He lets out a sigh of frustration.

"Nah Glend, maybe I'm just going crazy. Of course, I'll take you. I think I handled this wrong. Actually, now that I say it out loud, it sounds ridiculous. After hearing all the Britney/Kevin drama, I think anything is possible. Forget I ever said anything, I'll drop you off at the corner and you can walk the rest, so Ashley doesn't see my car." Thank god, I'm really not in the mood to walk all the way there.

"Yeah, well, Ashley isn't Britney.... You don't have to worry about anything. Stop being crazy!" I say.

He laughs and says, "Yeah, thank you Glend, you're right. I appreciate you, thank you for everything! I would offer to fuck one last time, but I'm taken hahaha" I laugh too and say, "Yeah, you are taken by a good girl, and a great friend of mine!" We finally arrive to the corner of Ashley's house. "Ok, well, I'm gonna get going, thanks for the ride Matt!" I say. "No worries Glend, if you need a ride home, just let me know! I'll probably be in the area in case Ashley wants to see me." I get out of the car and before closing the door I say, "I got you, I'll hit you up!" I walk towards Ashley's house still processing what happened. Why me?

Chapter 13

Matt really thinks Ashley would sleep with Kevin? He's way too paranoid. Ashley would never do something like that.
I'm laughing at the idea of it. That guilty conscious might be getting to him. I reach her house and the music is blasting. I text Ashley saying I'm outside. I'm waiting for a minute before she comes to open the door.
"Oh my god, I never get to see your mom! I wanted to say hi. Either way, come in, come in!" I come inside and see Ashley's mom in the kitchen making sure everything is running smoothly.
"Hey Glend, how are you? Don't mind me! I know I look like a crazy lady, but someone has to make sure everything is on point. How are the decorations?" She asks, looking proud of her work.
I look around and see Happy 50th Birthday signs everywhere, the whole house is decorated in black, silver and gold.
"I'm doing good, thank you! Yes, the house looks beautiful. Who's turning fifty?"
Ashley's mom pouts and says, "Ashley didn't tell you? It's her dad's birthday! He's turning fifty!"
I turn to Ashley and turn back at her mom and say, "No she didn't, I would've brought a gift I'm so sorry!"
Ashley rolls her eyes and says, "Glend, shut up. You're family, you don't have to get my dad a gift! Mom, stop stressing out. We're gonna go in my room while more people get here."
Ashley grabs my hand and leads me to her room.

Once we're in her room, she closes the door and lays on her bed. I go to lay next to her and she holds my hand. We're both staring at the ceiling in silence for five minutes.

"Glend, can I ask you something?" She says, finally breaking the silence. If I've learned anything from this past year, it's that nothing good comes from that question.

"Of course, what's up Ashley?" I respond.

"When did you know you were gay?" She asks, as we both continue looking at the ceiling.

"I've always known, I've always been attracted to guys since I can remember. The hard part was telling people, but luckily my mom never cared." I say. "And you've never liked girls? Have you ever tried being with a girl? If I were naked and asked you to hook up, would you do it? For educational purposes." She asks.

"Wow, this is random, but no, I've never found the urge to. I think you're beautiful, but if you were naked and asked me to hook up, I would still say no, because I'm not attracted to girls. I just like guys." Ashley just smiles.

"Why the sudden curiosity? Are you gonna confess your love for me? If so, can we wait until after the party to reject you? I really want some food!" I say, while letting out a laugh.

Ashley starts laughing too and says, "No, I'm not in love with you! I have this weird suspicion and I don't want to say it out loud, but nothing else makes sense. I hate saying it outloud so you'll be the second person I tell, can I trust you?"

I can only imagine where this is going, but at this point what can I say right? There's no way I said something when I was drunk right? I turn to look Ashley in the eyes. "Of course, what happened?" I ask.

Ashley is silent for about a minute and then says, "I think Matt is gay." I felt like my heart was going to explode out of my chest. "Why do you think he's gay?" We're both still looking at the ceiling and Ashley says, "There's a lot of reasons. We only fuck in the dark and have only done it a handful of times. He never wants to eat me out. He barely looks at me when I'm naked. One time, I was completely naked in his bed, and he just walked by and told me to put clothes on. I was so confused. I went through his phone and he's always saving guy's pictures on his phone. He told me it's gym inspiration, but I don't believe it." She's still not done, she just gasped for air but I'm the one who can't breathe.

"I thought he wasn't attracted to me, but someone told me that all his girlfriend's say the same thing. One of his ex's could've sworn she saw gay porn on his phone. Isn't that crazy?" She says.

"Yeah that's a lot, I'd never picture Matt being gay." I say. I know I'm a liar but don't judge me. I mean, this isn't the right time to confess that I slept with him before their date. I don't think there will ever be a right time, but especially now that Ashley has these many suspicions. Then it dawned on me.

"Wait, you said I'm the second person you told… who's the

first?" She grips my hand and closes her eyes. "Okay, well this is the part I didn't want to say… I asked Kevin!" She says.

I pause for a moment, turn, and then ask her, "Ashley, did you hook up with Kevin?" She turns to me and nods her head.
"Glend, I was so sex deprived. We keep fucking during lunch. He makes me cum in less than 10 minutes. You don't understand, Matt has never made me cum! I feel terrible, but I figured if he's gay, then it cancels each other out. Right?" I chuckle and say, "Yeah but, what if he isn't gay?" She puts a pillow over her head and lets out a huge scream.
"If he isn't gay, then I fucked up. I'm hoping he's gay. Glend, please don't tell anyone. I don't know how to tell him, but I'm going to one way or another. You know, if he is gay, maybe you can give him some pointers? Fuck, my boyfriend is gay. Well, at least I'm not Britney, right?" We both look at each other and let out a hysterical laugh.
"Nah, you're nothing like Britney, trust me. I would tell him as soon as you can but leave out the Kevin part. Just tell him what you're feeling. Maybe, he'll get so offended, he'll dump you, and we don't have to worry about it!" Ashley nods her head.
We lay there a little longer in silence when Ashley still has something on her mind. "Glend?" She asks. "Yeah?" I say.
"Thank you for being my best friend. I know you go through struggles that you don't tell me about, but I'm so grateful I have you in my life. You're always there when I need you the most. I hope you count on me as much as I count on you. I love you."

Okay, now my heart might rip out of my chest. It feels so good to feel loved by somebody the same way I love them.

"Thank you for being my best friend too. I will always be here for you. I love you too. Now, let's go party! I hear a lot of people coming through the door already." We hug and after Ashley says, "Just don't tell anyone about this. I'll figure it out. I always do!"

I look at her and say, "you have my word!" We both get up from the bed and leave the room.

An hour passes while Ashley and I mingle with her family. We dance, have some drinks, and play some games. It's still pretty early, and more people are expected to arrive. Hispanic parties are always loud and fun. They usually end at like two or three in the morning, but they're a hell of a good time. Everyone who comes just brings more alcohol. Ashley and I hear, "Ashley go get another bottle of tequila, your uncle is running out!" from across the party.

Ashley responds with, "Okay, going now!" I follow Ashley into the kitchen and ask her "Do you know who said that?" She turns around and says, "No idea, but they want tequila, so who am I to say no?" As Ashley is reaching for the bottle at their family bar, we hear a familiar voice.

"Oh my god, Ashley, your house is super cute!" Ashley and I both look at each other because we know exactly who's voice

that was. We turn around and see none other than Britney and X. I can tell
Ashley is as shocked as I am. "Babe, say hi. Don't be rude!" Britney says, as she hits X in the stomach. "Sup cuz, sup Glend. How are you guys?" He asks. I am at a loss for words but Ashley quickly responds with "Good, you guys want a drink?"

Britney lets out her obnoxious little laugh. "God yes, his parents wanted us to come so badly, so here we are." Britney looks around trying to judge Ashley's house but can't find anything to complain about. "You have a cute little house Ashley, not bad." She says. Wow, that didn't even sound like a compliment. "Yeah, my house is beautiful because of my mom. She put a lot of effort into it." Ashley whips back at her. I still haven't said a word. "Yo Ash, where's Tio at? I want to give him my gift and introduce him to Britney. My parents are out of town
and wanted me to pass by and give it to him." X says.
"I wish Tio and Tia were here! Maybe next time! My dad? He's in the back, go and look! He's loud, you'll find him. Excuse me, Glend and I have to get something from my mom's room. Have fun guys, make yourself at home!" Ashley says as she drags me to her mom's room. We speed walk into her mom's room with no hesitation. Once we're in the room, we both look at each other in disbelief. "What is he doing here? What is SHE doing here?" I ask. "Bro I was expecting his parents, but not him! He never comes to our family parties anymore. Glend is this my karma? I have to stare at Britney in the face, knowing I'm no better than she is! Oh my god, I even did it with the same guy!

I'm horrible! I'm the biggest hypocrite whore in the world." Ashley starts freaking out, so I grab her and say, "Calm down, we got this okay? Nobody knows anything.

We're going to get through tonight, and you're going to tell Matt. You're not a hypocritical whore like Britney. You're human and you're allowed to make mistakes. We're going to get through this night together! Got it?" I say. I'm somewhat manhandling her, but it seems she's calmed down. "Yes, let's get through tonight, and I'll break up with Matt tomorrow. Thank you.
We got this!" She says. We both look at each other and we know we'll get through this together! I wish Ashley knew she wasn't the only one having a meltdown right now.As we reenter the party, Ashley and I decide to at least have a shot, because we're dealing with a lot. X and Britney are in their own corner while Ashley and I keep drowning ourselves in shots and dancing our lives away. At some point, we even forget they are here. An hour passes, and we all gather around to sing Ashley's dad Happy Birthday. We take pictures, dance, and take some more shots. Ashley and I were having so much fun, that we forgot all about our troubles. We're both the right kind of drunk. Not too drunk that you're embarrassing, but not too sober that you're boring.
We're having a blast. Eventually, people start leaving. One of the first to leave are X and Britney. We see him say bye to Ashley's parents and head out. Ashley and I made sure to not be close by, so we don't have to awkwardly say bye to them.

Saying hi to them was enough. “Did they leave?” I ask while pouring another round of shots for me and Ashley.

“Yes, I saw them walk out. Thank God we barely saw them, they were in their zone, and we were in ours.” She says. “Honestly, I don’t care if Matt finds out about Kevin. I just prefer it coming from me, you know? It’s the least I can do.” I hand her a shot and say, “Cheers to the least we can do!” We drink up and continue partying.

By two thirty in the morning, the party is almost over. I told Matt to be here at this time because that’s the time I wanted to go home. Hopefully James is asleep already. He texted me and told me he’s waiting for me in the corner. “Glend, who’s taking you home? I want to make sure you get home safe, you’ve been drinking!” Ashley’s mom says, as she starts picking up trash.

“My mom’s picking me up! She’s actually at the corner now. Where’s Ashley?” I ask.

“She knocked out on her bed, she’s too far gone.” Her mom responds.

I laugh and say, “Yeah, I just noticed she’s been gone a while. Thank you for having me! Have a good night!”

As I walk out the door I hear, “Good night sweetie, thank you for coming. You’ll always be family for us! Text me when you’re home!” Then she closed the door behind me. I’m walking towards the corner and it’s like all the alcohol is hitting me at once. With every step, it’s like I’m getting drunker and drunker. This feels so weird, because I was fine a few minutes ago.

Maybe my mind was scared of Ashley's mom, so it pretended to be sober.
Anyways, I'm walking towards Matt's car and I'm pretty lit.
Matt unlocks the door and I get in the passenger seat.
"How was the party?" He asks.

"Honestly, it was a lot of fun. I'm trashed and Ashley is knocked the fuck out. That being said, we had so much fun despite some people being there!" I say as I struggle to put my seat belt on.
Matt starts driving me home and asks, "What people?"
I temporarily sober up and say, "Just some of Ashley's relatives. You don't know them."
He nods his head and asks, "Did she say anything about me?"
I take my phone out and say, "No, she didn't talk about you at all."
He nods again and says, "alright bet."
The drive to my house seems like forever. We're at a stop light, so I decide to make some conversation.
"Thanks for taking me home, I owe you." I say.
"No problem, don't worry about it." He says. I'm pretty drunk so
I want to make this a little juicy, fuck it. Let's see if Ashleys suspicions are half right, or all the way right. "Sooo…..since only you and I know, am I the only guy you've ever been with?" I ask. He turns to me and says, "Yeah, you're the only guy I've ever been with." I pucker my lips and nod my head.
"And, you don't think of fucking another guy?" I ask. "Nah, I just think of fucking you." We both lock eyes, and he continues

talking. I think I'm about to have some fun. Matt can probably tell how drunk I am but he's gassing me up.
"It was the best sex I've ever had. I think about it all the time. I wish I had a video or something." He starts licking his lips.
"Yeah? What was your favorite part?" I ask. The light turns green, so he begins to drive.

"Your head was magical. Feeling my dick hit the back of your throat, was amazing. Next, your tight little hole." He forms a fist and bites it. "I just want to feel you one last time." He says. As he's driving, he puts his hand on my thigh. "Just one last time would be enough for me." I'm pretty turned on, but I can't. I just act like I don't notice it. We get to my house, and I think really hard, with my right head. I move his hand, look at him and say, "This is hot and you were a good fuck, but no orgasm is worth the friendship Ashley and I have. Hit me up when you're single." He let out a sigh and said, "the fact that you're a good friend, makes
me want you ten times more. Understood though. If I'm ever single, I'll hit you up." We both shake hands and I get out of the car. I'm pretty proud of myself. Even being drunk, I made a good decision. I walk up to my trailer ready for bed. I walk in and see my stepdad drinking on the couch. "Didn't I tell you to sleep at your friend's house?" He says, as I walk in. "I told you and my mom I wasn't going to." I say while making my way to the kitchen.
"Yeah that's right, you know I had to slap the fuck out of your mom today because of how she talked to me." Oh no, he's being

drunk and aggressive. He's in one of those moods and I have nowhere to run. If I just ignore him, he'll get up and go to sleep. He throws an empty beer can at me, and it hits my head. He starts uncontrollably laughing.

"You know, I never realized why your mom loves a faggot like you. I think of all the problems that would be solved if I didn't have you on my couch. I tell her all the time we should kick your little gay ass out, and just live alone together. She's almost done it a few times but ends up backing down. I have to ask myself, how can she love you?

How can anyone love you? I never see you with any friends. Everyone probably knows you're just a little faggot." I know I'm supposed to just ignore him, but his words hurt so much that I begin to cry.

The tears do nothing to stop James from being aggressive towards me.

"Aww is the little faggot going to cry? Here, let me give you a real reason to cry." He says, as he gets up and charges at me.

"No,

please don't. I'm sorry." I beg while grabs me by my hair.

"You're not sorry. You don't fucking get it, do you?! Nobody loves you and nobody will ever love you. You are nothing but a burden to everyone. Tonight, I'm going to teach you how to respect." He shouts. The grip on my hair gets tighter and tighter with every insult.

"Please, I'm sorry, I just want to go to sleep. Please James, I'm sorry I was born. I'm so sorry." I say with tears streaming down my face. James throws me to the floor and begins kicking me. I try to cover myself but it's no use. He's bigger, and stronger than me, so I'll never be able to overpower him. I scream for help, but my mom is in too much of a drunk sleep to hear me. He tires out after a few more kicks and walks over to get his beer.

"You see Glend, you're nothing, and you'll always be nothing. You deserve to be on the floor, beaten down, faggots like you are a curse to this world." He finishes his beer, washes his hands, and walks to his room, stopping just before he entered. He was kicking me with his construction boots, so he begins to take them off.

Finally, he turns to me and says, "When you're done fucking around, clean up this mess." As he walks in his room, he throws both boots at me, laughs, and closes the door. I am in so much pain right now.

Every inch of my body hurts. I lay there, wondering if what he's saying is true. Maybe I do deserve to die. What if I just kill myself, since I'm such a burden to everyone? Maybe the world is better off without me. What if death is the solution? I lay there for about ten more minutes and try to get up. After several failed attempts, I get up despite the horrible pain. I walk towards the mirror we have in the kitchen, and just stare at myself. I look all beaten up. He kicked my face, so my mouth is bleeding, and I can already see the black eyes forming. I take my shirt off and see that I have bruises all over my stomach. It hasn't even been twenty minutes and I'm already seeing the marks, so I know tomorrow, they will look horrible. I'm supposed to work too, how am I supposed to go to work like this?

My eyes begin tearing up as I stare at my empty living room. What did I do to deserve this? Does anyone else live like this? Why don't I have a normal life?

Every inch of my body hurts. I just had such a good night, and I came home to get beat on. Why me? I clean my face up and then the mess James made. My mouth is still bleeding. I think my lip is busted. My entire shirt is drenched in blood. I sit down on my couch and think about everything James just said to me. Is this life worth living? Why is it that I can never be happy? Every time something good happens, something horrible follows. Maybe

James is right, maybe if I didn't exist everyone's problems would be solved.

Even this love triangle thing I'm in wouldn't exist if I just died. I wish I had another life. James is already snoring, but how can I sleep when I'm in this much pain? I just want to slit my wrists and end it all.

I slowly walk into the kitchen and get a knife. I sit on the couch again and decide that I'm going to end my life. I'm tired of this existence. Maybe if I kill myself, I'll be able to live a brand new life. Maybe I'll be reborn and have a happy life with a family that truly loves me. I decide that the only person I'm going to say bye to is Ashley. I want to tell her the truth about everything. I find my phone under the couch and realize it's been dead for a while.

I plug it in to charge and make mental notes of what I'm going to tell Ashley. I know I want to tell her everything from X to Britney to Matt. Hopefully, she'll know what to do with that information. Is that selfish? Should I just keep it to myself? My phone powers on and a flood of messages start coming in. They're all from an unknown number. I start reading and recognize it's X texting me from a texting app.

"I don't know if I'm blocked but I need to talk to you. Please call me when you can."

"Please call me."

"Glend I dropped Britney off, please text me." I take a deep breath before calling him. I love X, I need to say my goodbyes.

"Hello?" he answers.

"Hey, I'll make this short. My stepdad just beat me really hard and I have officially lost the will to live. I'm killing myself tonight and I just wanted to tell you I love you so much. I hope you find someone who makes you happy all day every day."

I say as I begin to cry. Why did I just tell him that? I'm the only one who could make him happy.

I'm broken and as much pain as I'm in, there's relief in speaking my truth. X is still in shock from what he just heard.

"Glend! Wait, wait wait! Calm down! You don't have to kill yourself, please calm down!" He says.

"I do have to kill myself. Nobody will ever love someone like me.

I'm better off dead. Everyone will be so much happier." I say while crying hysterically.

"Nobody will ever love someone like you? I love you. You're the first thing I think of in the morning, and the last thing I think about before I go to sleep. I want to talk to you every minute of every day. My whole day brightens up when I see you. You are my light, please don't leave me. Look, I'm going to go over and see you!

Stay on the phone with me okay?" I can hear him starting to turn his car on.

I continue hysterically crying, then I calm down enough to say, "Okay, I'll wait." I'm sitting on my kitchen floor with a knife in one hand and my phone in another. Was I really about to kill myself? I've never gotten to this point before. Was this my breaking point? Does it get better or worse from here? What do I do?

"Baby, you there?" X says.

"Yeah, I'm here." I say, with a voice equally as broken as my spirit. A few minutes pass and I hear a knock on the door. I open the door and see X completely relieved to see me. He gives me the biggest hug.

"Please don't kill yourself. I love you. I love you so much baby. I'm sorry I put you through so much. You're my whole world. God, I can't imagine a life without you."

He holds me tightly and makes sure I know how sincere he's being. We hug for a few more minutes before he pulls away slightly.

He wipes some of my tears and asks, “you feel better?” I nod and lay my head on his chest.

“Where’s your stepdad?” He asks.

“He’s sleeping with my mom in the room.” I say.

“You are literally covered in bruises. I should kill him. Actually, no…I am going to kill him.” He says with one foot in the door. Seeing how angry X is gets me so overwhelmed, and I start crying again. “Please don’t do anything, I don’t want any more problems. I just want to sleep peacefully.” I say, as I wipe my tears. I stare into his eyes, and I can see how him seeing me cry, is breaking his heart. He takes one deep breath and says, “Let’s go, you’ll sleep at my house tonight. I’m not going to leave you here. Don’t worry about clothes because I have. Tomorrow is Saturday, so you probably work. I’ll call them and tell them you can’t come in because you’re sick. You never call out, so they won’t mind. You don’t even need a phone charger, I got you. I will always be here for you until the day I die. Got it?” He says, as he begins to hug me. “Ok, let’s go” I say, with no hesitation.

“Get your keys and your phone, let’s go.” He says as he walks to unlocks his car. I already had my phone, so I just had to get my keys.

I find my keys as quickly as possible, lock the door, and run to X’s car. He drives off as fast as possible. I know he’s pissed off, but I didn’t want him to make the situation worse. He’s driving so recklessly, and I know it’s because he’s furious right now.

Honestly, you can tell how mad a guy is by how reckless they drive. The more reckless they drive, the angrier they are.

He's speeding to get to his house, but with the way he's driving, I'm glad James didn't hear him. I can't imagine what would've happened. Before I know it, we're in his driveway. He turns the car off and we sit in silence for about 5 minutes. I honestly feel like he's going to express his anger towards me. I know I didn't do anything to him, but he's so angry I'm scared, like it's James sitting in the driver seat.

He turns to me with tears and says, "I'm sorry I let this happen to you. I should be there to protect you. I should be there for you all the time. I'm such an idiot, I fucked everything up. Please forgive me. Maybe I should've tried harder." In between the tears and the words, he's lifting my shirt and getting a good look at me.

"God, you're bruised everywhere, what if you're hurt really badly? I should've never dated Britney. God. I'm such a fucking idiot. I can't believe it." He really shouldn't have, but I'm in too much pain to be petty right now. As we sit in X's car, he's still sitting there in disbelief telling me all the things I wish he would've said months ago, before I fucked Matt.

"Seeing you like this breaks my heart. Please forgive me, I love you. Please don't ever kill yourself. I need you alive. I need to know you're alive. God. I'm such a fucking IDIOT. Glend, I promise, I'll make this right. I love you baby, please don't ever feel like no one ever loves you. I love you with all my heart." He's telling me all this with tears in his eyes and a face full of guilt.

I can't let X think he has anything to do with what happened tonight. I will not guilt him into being mine.
I grab his hand and calmly say, "What happened tonight wasn't your fault. It had nothing to do with you. My stepdad always does this to me. I just hit my breaking point today. Thank you for being there for me, but I'm not going to guilt you either.
I love you too, and now that I'm calm, I realize how much I wasn't thinking. It was a combination of my emotions, my physical pain, and his words. This isn't your fault my love. I love you, and I'm not going to hurt myself." One thing about X, he takes my words extremely seriously. I immediately feel him calming down.
I hold his hand tight and say, "I love you."
He kisses my hand and says, "I love you more." We sit for a few minutes and once we're calm he says, "What a fucked up situation right?" while laughing.
I can't help but laugh a little too.
"Yeah, this wasn't how I expected us to talk again. Well, I didn't think we were ever gonna talk again." He starts laughing.
"Are you crazy?! We're always going to go back to each other. One way or another. Our love is too real."
He gives me another kiss and says, "Let's get inside so we can shower you, you're covered in blood. I'll take care of you tonight baby." He says with a smile. He rushes out of the car and opens the door.

“Here, I’m going to carry you up, you shouldn’t be walking.” He puts me in his arms and gives me a kiss.
“What if someone sees us?” I ask.
“I don’t give a fuck right now.” He says, as he carries me inside.
We get to the door, and I ask, “How are you gonna open the door?”
He looks at me and says, “I didn’t think that much through.” We both laugh and he puts me down. He unlocks the door and leads me to his bathroom. He takes off both of our clothes. He gets the tub ready for a bubble bath, and he begins bathing me.
He holds me tight and says, “I never want to let you go. I love you so much baby.” X hugs me from the back and begins crying.

“I can’t believe I almost lost you today. I’d never forgive myself. Please, if you ever feel like doing something like that again, call me. Whether we’re talking or not, I’ll listen to you. I’ll always be here for you, my forever love.” His words are so amazing, they’re exactly what I need to hear.
X makes me calm; he brings me a real peace I can’t find anywhere else.
“It’s funny, every time something happens we always end up back in your house. Sometimes I feel like it’s our escape from reality.” I say. He hugs me tighter.
“Wanna go to bed my love?” he asks. I nod my head and he gets us each a towel to dry ourselves. He gets up from the tub and he dries me before he dries himself.

"You know you're wetting the floor right?" I say with a laugh. X looks down and starts laughing. "Yeah I guess I am but, drying you is way more important right now." He says. "I can dry myself babe, dry yourself so we don't make a mess in the bathroom." I grab the towel and finish drying myself.

"I don't have any clothes here." I say.

He smirks and says, "I guess we'll just sleep naked until I figure it out." We walk to his room and lay in his bed.

He wraps himself around me and says, "I don't want to do anything else but hold you all night. You are my eternal love." As he holds me tight, I begin falling asleep in his arms. I'm in absolute heaven. James broke my spirit tonight, and the last person I thought would save me, saved me.

Chapter 14

The next morning, I wake up and realize, it isn't a dream. I'm in X's room, next to X, as he sleeps. My body is still sore from my stepdad's beating, but nothing I can't handle. I can tell my lip is swollen, but that'll go down by the time I have to go to school on Monday. I turn around and see X peacefully asleep.
He's so beautiful. Everything about him, I truly cannot believe. I'm laying next to such a beautiful man. Our journey hasn't been easy, but we always end up back with each other. Like I've always said, our relationship isn't perfect, but it's what we have. He came to my rescue last night, that's what matters. I'm so in love, it's crazy. My beautiful man, he deserves some type of pleasure. I'll wake him up to some head. He's sleeping, but his dick is hard. I go under the covers and just start going to work. I shove it completely in my mouth. I start sucking while stroking, a little trick I like to call the washing machine. I can tell he's waking up because he starts grabbing the back of my head.
"Baby,
pleaseeeee, oh my god." He moans. I go faster and harder. I'm going to make sure I please my man. "Babe…. I'm gonna ahhhhh." X busts in my mouth, and I swallow it whole. "Jesus Christ, baby, I wasn't expecting that. Good morning!" He says, with a relieved face. "Good morning baby, it was the least I could do after last night. I love you." I say, before giving him a kiss. "I

love you too baby, I'm going to make some breakfast and call your job. Lemme get you some clothes" X gets up, wipes the little bit of cum he had left off, and starts handing me clothes.

We both get dressed and head to the kitchen. X calls my job and asks to speak directly to Monica. "Yeah Glend isn't
feeling too well. He has a horrible fever and he's passed out. I can bring you guys a doctor's note if you want. No? alrighty, again, I'm sorry. When he feels better, I'll tell him to call you guys.
Thank you Monica, have a great day." He hangs up and hands me my phone.
"Monica is really nice, she seemed really concerned about you." He says, as he starts frying some eggs.
"Yeah, she's awesome. She's the only one who notices me at work. She's the best manager ever." I say.
"Look Glend, I know there's something going on, so I'm going to ask you to be honest with me, and don't lie like there isn't. What's going on with you? What's bothering you so much? Yesterday was your breaking point and I'm glad I was there, but what if next time you don't call me? I want to try to fix the issue, so you don't go down that road ever again. I need you to talk." He says. I'm silent for a few minutes so I can gather my thoughts. "I'm very unhappy with a lot of aspects in my life. My home, my relationship with you, the fact that I'm keeping everyone's secrets, but no one is thinking of me. I carry all these

burdens, hoping no one gets hurt, meanwhile I get hurt every day.

I want to say the secrets have taken a huge toll on me, but I hope he doesn't ask too many questions. I'm giving him the truth though so I can't leave anything out.

"Every day, someone comes up to me and tells me to keep their secret. Most of the time, I don't even want to know. I'm just at the wrong place at the wrong time. It's exhausting." I say, as he continues cooking.

"I can't vent to anyone about anything, I feel like I have no one." He puts the eggs on a plate and starts cooking bacon.

"Do you feel like you can't vent to me because the secrets will hurt me?"He turns to me and asks. "Yeah it will hurt you." I say, as I nod.

"Alright, let's try this. I'm going to do things right this time. I want you to vent everything you're keeping bottled up. You tell me every secret, and I promise I won't be mad at you. You're the love of my life, and these secrets are taking too much of a toll on you.

We'll start with the secrets, and then work on everything else in due time. Deal?" X puts the plate of food in front of me as he waits for a response.

I'm nervous because if I start talking I'm going to want to say everything.

Here goes nothing. "And you won't get mad at me? Or tell someone I told you?" I ask.
"I can't promise it won't get me mad, but I won't be directly mad at you, and I won't address anyone about anything. Everything
you tell me at this table stays here. If it's this or your life, I pick your life over and over. One day, you and I will be married with kids in another state away from all of this. If this leads us one step closer then so be it." He says as he picks his food. Omg married with kids!? I take a deep breath and start.

"Okay I'm going to tell you everything from the beginning. I don't know when it started but Britney was cheating on you with Kevin." Okay so far, so good, X took that one well.
"At the party we saw you guys at, she fucked Kevin in a room while Ashley and I were hiding. She came and told you she was pregnant with your baby, but it was really Kevin's baby.
She got drunk at minigolf and told me. She said she just needed money for an abortion, so that's why she said it was yours." I pause because I can see X is already getting mad. That last one seemed to have hit a nerve. "I can stop if you want." I say to him.
He composes himself and says "No, I need to know the truth. Keep going, if this is helping you then, so be it. Keep going." I wait a few seconds and then I continue. Time to say the one thing I didn't want to tell him. Even more than knowing Britney lied about the baby being his. "I slept with Matt on Valentine's Day, before he went on a date with Ashley. I didn't know he was

going on a date with her, so him and I both promised to not tell Ashley. Everything was going good, but now Ashley suspects that Matt is gay, because he is, so now she's sleeping with Kevin at lunch to get back at him." X's mouth completely drops.

"You slept with MATT?! THAT UGLY DORK?! Oh my god, I'm gonna kill him. No, I'm going to actually murder him.
I'm gonna be on the news. WAIIIIT, Ashley doesn't know? Oh my god I just want to beat the fuck out of this dork.

You cheated on me with MATT? WHO ELSE HAVE YOU CHEATED ON ME WITH? ARE YOU SERIOUS?" X starts pacing back and forth while yelling. "No, Ashley doesn't know but she's breaking up with him today. I only slept with him once even though he tried last night. Also, I technically didn't cheat on you. If you consider that cheating, you were with Britney that night. We weren't even together. I've never cheated on you.
I also haven't slept with anyone else." I say, as I sit calmly. He puts his hands on his hips and continues pacing. Maybe this honesty thing wasn't such a good idea.
Watching everything click in X's head is different. I don't know how to explain it. I don't know if I'm turned on or scared.
"Wait?! He tried last night? Yeah I'm gonna kill him. When I see him, he's dead. Who does that fucking dork think he is? He's just a fucking bozo." I can't help but chuckle.

"You think this is funny?! I'm about to end up on the news!" He says.
"Yeah, it's funny. You're not going to do anything, because you promised. It's just a lot of information to process at once. I get it, imagine how long I've been holding on to this." I say, as I eat my breakfast. "And this bitch was pregnant with Kevin's baby? And used me?! And you knew?! What the fuck was that about?" He asks.
"You wouldn't have listened to me anyways. Technically, you guys were just supposed to abort the baby and part ways, but you guys decided to get together again. I also make everything about me, so why would you believe me? Right?" I say while finishing the last bit of food.

X breathes in and out a few times and says, "Okay, that was a lot. I can barely stand after 5 minutes, and you've been holding on to this for months? Jesus Christ. Now that I'm calm, you don't have to worry about anything. I was going to end things with Britney anyways, but now I don't have to feel bad. I'll just tell her I'm not feeling her, and I think the baby blinded me. Just don't keep these many secrets from me again, start pillow talking, Jesus Christ. Deal?!" He says.
I look up to him and say, "Deal! No more secrets! To be honest I don't know why you made the Matt thing such a big deal, it's not that serious."
X chuckles and says, "Oh yeah? It's not a big deal? You wouldn't get mad if I hooked up with someone you know?" I

roll my eyes and say, “You already did, how much worse can I get? And I don’t think I would handle it like such a baby!”
He licks his lips, smirks and says, “Ashley told you that her and I lost our virginities to each other right?” My eyes have never opened wider.
“Excuse me? Are you serious?” I ask in disgust.
“Yeah, I’m totally serious. Ashley and I have always been fuck buddies, but she told you that right?” he replies. I pause because I know I have to handle this with grace and maturity.
Let’s be serious though, my emotions get the best of
me, and I begin snapping on X. “ARE YOU FUCKING SERIOUS?! YOU USED TO HOOK UP WITH ASHLEY? OH MY GOD,
WHO HAVEN’T YOU HOOKED UP WITH. JUST GO WITH THE WHOLE SCHOOL WHY DON’T YA? JESUS CHRIST.”

I continue to blow up, but I might have just given X a reason to snap himself. “YOU’RE ONE TO TALK. ME, MATT, WHO KNOWS HOW MANY OTHER GUYS THERE ARE. GO FUCK KEVIN, MIGHT AS WELL.” He says as he approaches me. We’re both looking at each other from across the dining table. Our eyes are filled with anger and passion.
“You want me to go fuck Kevin?” I ask.
He gets closer and says “I’ll fucking kill him. Come here.” And starts passionately kissing me. Before I know it, we’re making love on his dining table.He asks me a different question with every stroke.

"You're mine baby, you got that? No one else's. No one can fuck you but me…got it?" He's literally pounding me and the tight little hole he loves.

"I'm gonna cum all in you, because you're mine.. I SAID GOT IT?" His strokes are getting harder.

"Yes, I'm yours baby, I'm all yours." I respond while getting plowed. His strokes are so rough I can't concentrate. He's pounding me so hard I can't see colors; all I see is black and white. A few more strokes and he finishes in me.

He gives me a deep kiss and says, "Okay, no more secrets. Deal?" I'm literally filled with his cum and say, "Deal, I have to shower again, I have cum in my ass."

He slaps my ass and says, "Yeah, my cum. Go wash up baby." I go shower and change into new clothes again.

"So what are we going to do today?" I ask X.

"Well, my parents said they won't be back until Wednesday so, you can stay here until then, because I do not want you going home. I know you work tomorrow, so I'll take you to work and pick you up. There's a party tonight, but I'd much rather stay here, just watch romantic comedies, and eat our favorite meal. What do you think?" He asks. I can't help but smile from ear to ear.

"Sounds like a perfect date." X and I spent our entire Saturday together after that. We laid up on the couch, watching movies all day. The only time X used his phone was to end things with Britney for good.

"It's over and that's final. I'm not going back and forth with you. I thought I wanted this, but I just want to be alone." He says to her on the phone. "Put it on speaker!" I whisper. He puts it on speaker and mutes the phone. All you can hear is her bawling.

"Please don't do this, what can I do to make this right? Please, I'm begging you. You're the love of my life. Don't leave me. I swear I didn't do anything wrong. We had a baby together, did you forget?" X and I can't stop laughing.

"Hello? Are you still there?" She asks. X shushes me and unmutes the phone.

"Brit, I don't want anything to do with you. We're done. Please don't make this any harder than what is already is. It's done. Goodbye." He says and hangs up. Two hours pass by, and I realize I haven't seen my phone since X called Monica.

"Babe, where's my phone?" I ask.

He was really into the movie but eventually says, "I think I left it on the kitchen counter babe, I don't know, this part is really good, go check." I get up and see my phone has been getting blown up all day. I have over thirty missed calls from my mom, five missed calls from Ashley and two missed calls from Matt. The only one who texted me was Ashley and she said, "You're probably busy right now, but I really need a friend tonight. Can we hang out?" The message was sent 20 minutes ago so I still have time to reply.

I want to be there for Ashley. I reply saying, "Yeah, I

could go now if you want?" and not even a minute passes before she replies with, "Please, I need you." Wow, another person needing me. This is amazing. I do have people that need me in their life. Fuck James.

"Babeeeee, I'm going to hang out with Ashley, she really needs a friend right now." I say. X is completely focused on the tv.

"Babe did you hear me?!" I sternly ask. He realizes he was distracted and solely focuses on me.

"Yes babe, I heard you, go hang with Ashley, but remember I still have to take you to work tomorrow. You're sleeping here right?" He asks.

"Yeah, I'm just going to hang with Ashley for a little and then I'll tell you to pick me up in a corner or something, I don't know. Can you actually drop me off at the corner of her house right now?" I say while I put my shoes on. X gets up and gives me a kiss.

"Yes, of course my love. You're such a good friend, I'm so happy
I met you. I love you." He says as he gets his keys.

"I love you more. Let's go so I can come back sooner." I say before I give him one big kiss. I text Ashley, and told her I'm on the way. X lives pretty close to Ashley so we take the long way before getting to the corner of her house. "I'm not going to give you a kiss, but I'll text you when to start heading out. I love you, see you later." I say, as I get out of the car. I walk towards Ashley's house and get a message from X.

"I love you more. Hurry up. I don't wanna be away from you too long." I can't help but smile at cute shit like this. I get to Ashley's house and knock on the door. Ashley's mom opens and is so happy to see me. "Thank God you're here Glend, she hasn't left her room all day. I'm starting to get worried. I even offered to take her to the mall and buy her whatever she wants, and she didn't want to go. That's when I knew something was up. I think you're the only one who can go in there and get her out of this funk. Come in please!" I come in and give her a kiss on the check as she continues to rant.

"Jesus, I'm sorry, how are you? Wait, what happened to you? Why are you all bruised up? What happened to your lip?? Do I have to murder someone? Or call the police? I can't deal with all of this. You kids are too much. I'm going to have a heart attack." I let out a chuckle and say, "Don't worry. I got into a fight but nothing I couldn't handle." Before I can continue, Ashley's mom hugs me tightly and begins to cry. "Don't cry! I'm fine and you're gonna be fine when I get Ashley out of this funk."

She lets me go and wipes her tears. "I got this! I'll be right back!" I say as I walk towards Ashley's room and knock on her door.

"Ashley? It's Glend can I come in?" I ask. "Yes, come in." She says very lightly. I come in and see she's laying down facing the ceiling.

I hate seeing Ashley like this. “Can I lay next to you?” I ask. She looks at me and asks, “Can you please lay next to me?” I take my shoes off and cuddle in next to her and she holds my hand as we both stare at the ceiling.

“Do you think I’m a bad person?” She asks me.

“No, I think you’re an amazing person actually.” I answer her, almost immediately.

“I spoke to Matt, and he told me a lot. Is there anything you want to tell me?” She asks. I was hesitant at first, but I answered with,

“How much did he tell you?”

She immediately answers with “He told me everything.” Omg I hope she doesn’t hate me. We lay in silence for a while until I get the courage to ask, “Are you mad at me?”

She turns to me and says, “At first, yeah I was. I was furious, but Matt explained how everything happened. He even told me how he tried hooking up with you last night and you said no. I realized that you’re actually a good friend and I’m a bad person.” Ashley begins to cry and my heart breaks. Ashley is always so bubbly and happy so seeing her cry isn’t something for the faint of heart.

Omg Ashley please stop, I cant.

“Hey, don’t cry. You’re not a bad person. You’re an amazing person. You help me out in so many ways, you have no idea. You did a bad thing, but that doesn’t make you a bad person. We all make mistakes. Did Matt understand?" I ask. She wipes her tears and says, "He's not mad at me, but he said when he sees Kevin, he's dead. I ruined a friendship of over 10 years." I let go of her hand and say, "No, you didn't ruin it. Kevin ruined it. It happened, and there's no going back, but we can go forward and make sure we don't make the same mistakes. I should've told you the second I found out you were dating Matt. I don't want to keep secrets from you. You're my best friend." I say to her. "I just feel like no one trusts me." She says.

I turn to her and say, "Get up! I trust you and I'm going to prove it to you. I'm going to tell you my biggest secret and I know you'll keep it, because that's what best friends do. Right?" She sits up and says, "Right. What's your secret?" I take a deep breath and start telling her about X. I go over everything from our beginning, to him dating Britney, and all the way to him dropping me off at her house today.

It takes about an hour to explain everything. By the time I'm done, Ashley is in complete shock. She hasn't said a word the entire time I've been explaining. She had absolutely no questions while I was telling her everything. Just shock. "And when I'm done here, he's going to pick me up and we're going to spend the night together.... Again." I finish explaining, and just wait for

Ashley's reaction.

She blinks a few times and says, "I never saw this coming. Did he tell you anything about me?" I chuckle. "Yeah he told me about you guys, he tells me
everything." Her mouth drops. "Oh my god it is true, we've never told anyone before. I'm in shock. I never saw this coming. You don't have to worry, I won't tell him or anyone anything, but oh my god! You really got me with that one. I have nothing to say. Wow, but I'm so happy for you guys, has he thought of coming out?" I let out a big laugh. "That's one of our problems remember, but we're getting there. But you see, I'm the bad guy in someone's story too. Britney doesn't even know I'm the reason they're not together. We all make mistakes. We just gotta keep it pushing and try to do better." Ashley has an epiphany mid conversation.

"Oh my god, do I attract gay guys? Am I like, a magnet? Is that a thing?" She starts freaking out.

"Calm down bro, you're not a gay magnet. I don't even think that's a thing. I never hooked up with Kevin! So, you're good." I say.

She starts thinking and says, "Yeah, you're right! I'm a good fuck,
I know I am! And I'm a good person too, fuck that!" She's starting to feel like herself again. Thank God.

Chapter 15

Ashley and I are sitting here in her room after a long school year, as survivors. We let our high school drama shake us up a little, but here we are, besties, getting through it all together.
"Thank you Glend, you really did make my day brighter.
I don't know what I'd do without you. I really need you." There it is. The sense of being needed. Someone in this world needs me.
Nothing tops this feeling. "I need you too, I love you."
We hug and Ashley says, "I love you more." In the midst of our hug, we feel a phone vibrating.
"Who's phone is that?" I ask.
"It's mine, oh my god, it's Kevin! He's calling me. Do I answer?" she asks. "Yes, answer and put it on speaker!" I say.
She answers and put it on speaker. We immediately hear Kevin say, "Yo Ashley."
She was hesitant at first but responded saying, "Yeah?" He immediately responds with, "So you told Matt huh? I was pretty mad at first, but I was really feeling you. Let me get a chance to do this right. Can I take you on a date tonight?" Ashley and I both look at each other and we nod our heads.
"Yeah, that sounds awesome. What time?" She asks.
Kevin says, "Be ready by 9:00, wear heels. I ain't gonna treat you like no second choice. Shit, you're my first choice. I'll hit you up later, I gotta make some moves, dale." and hangs up.
Ashley and I both start screaming. What the fuck is our life!?

my fucking I look at Ashley and say, "Did that just happen?! Oh god!!!!!" We both are screaming at the top of our lungs. Ashley's mom eventually barges in.

"What happened is everything okay?!" She asks, with a worried look on her face. "Yes mom, everything is alright. I have a date tonight, so we need to go to the mall like right now! I have nothing to wear." Ashley's mom looks so relieved. "Okay, that's my daughter. Thank you Glend, I was about to call the national guard. There's no love like a mother's love, and we know when something's wrong. It's our second nature." Speaking of a mother's love, I just remembered my mom has been calling me all day. I take my phone out of my pocket and see I have 20 more missed calls from her. I should at least answer her to let her know
I'm alright. "Guys, I'm gonna call my mom really quickly, gimmie a sec." I walk in the bathroom and call my mom. "Hello? Glend? Are you okay?" She sounds really worried. "Yeah mom, I'm okay I stayed at my friend's house. Yesterday was a lot." She sounds so relieved to hear me. "Oh my god, I saw the mess and all the blood on the floor. Glend, I'm sorry James did that. I kicked him out this morning, and he took all his stuff.
It's just us two. He really crossed a line yesterday, and I won't forgive him. I'm a mother before anything. I love you so much, I really do. You're my whole world. I need you to be okay, I don't know what I'd do without you." Wow, three times in one day?

She needs me too? James is a liar. He can't beat me mentally or emotionally, only physically.

"Thank you mommy, he really hurt me, but I love you too, and I'm always going to be here. I'm fine, I'm just at a friend's house, I'll let you know when I'm going home. I'm fine.
Don't worry.
Nothing I can't handle. It's just us two. Right?" I ask.

"Just us two, my love, call me when you're coming. Be safe. I love you." I don't know what's in the air today, but everyone's telling me how much they need me. I almost ended my life yesterday, thinking no one cared, and I have three people who care about me and need me. I was such an idiot. I feel the tears streaming down my face. Ah shit, it looks like I'm crying.
This is what it feels like to be loved. It's beautiful. X eventually picks me up at the corner of Ashley's house and we head to my house to pick up work clothes for tomorrow. I tell him how my mom kicked
James out and he's happy for me.
"Babe, this is awesome. You see, you matter to everyone. Things are looking up for us. One way or another, we're going to get through this." When we go pick up my clothes, my mom gives me the biggest hug. "I was so worried; I don't know what I'd do if something happened to you. Don't worry, James is gone for good." She says, as she gives me a kiss on the forehead. "Who's the hunk in the car?" She asks. "Mom he's just my friend." I say.

"Yeah, a friend I'm sure. Be careful, Glend. Call me if anything. Tell your friend I said hi, and I want to meet him one day." I kiss my mom goodbye and run to X's car.
"Your mom is beautiful, you know that right?" He says, as I get in the car. "Thanks babe, she wants to meet you one day. Step by step. Right?" I say, with the biggest grin on my face. "Right baby" He says, as he drives off. We ate, watched some Romcoms, and fell asleep in each other's arms when the night came.

The next day, I walk into my store, ready to tell Monica the rollercoaster of my life. I'm sure she's ready to hear the madness. I look around for her, but she's nowhere to be found. That's strange since she's usually here before me. I go to the break room and ask another cashier "Have you seen Monica?" He looked confused and said, "Didn't you hear? Yesterday was her last day. We threw a party for her and everything. Everyone was wondering where you were." Wow, my heart is broken. "No, I didn't know, I was really busy yesterday. That sucks, I didn't get to say bye." I start walking towards my locker and get a little sad. Monica was the first person to give me advice about X. She was always so sweet. I'm really going to miss her. I wish I could've said bye. I open my locker and there's a letter for me. "Dear Glend, if you're reading this, we didn't get our formal goodbye. I got accepted into my dream school. Everything happened so fast, before I knew it, it was my last day at the store.

I was really hoping to see you, but I think I would've cried my eyes out. You truly are a kind child. You made working at that store the biggest pleasure. No one is a beast at the cash register like you are! I left you my number to text me in case you ever have problems with that dreamy boy. I wish you the best with him, I think he's good for you, but there's a lot of work to be done. I'm sure you'll figure it out. I'm still in Florida. It's a city called Gainesville. If you're ever in town, call me! Take care and be the best possible version of yourself! I'll be expecting a text from you soon! 'Til next time! – Love, Monica"

That was so sweet. Monica is truly an angel in my life.

I save her number knowing I'll text her when I get out of work. I definitely need to stay in contact with her. I put the note in my bag before putting it in the locker. My shift flies by, and without Monica, I didn't have anyone to distract me. I finish closing up quickly and walk straight to the spot where X picks me up. I get in the car and tell him how Monica left for her dream school.

"What's the name of the city again?" He asks. "Gainesville. It's in Northern Florida." I say.

"Ohhh, I know where that is. Yeah, those college towns are always wild. You should look into cities like that, I think you'd like it." He says. "I've never thought of ever leaving Miami, that sounds scary." I say. "Well, if you go, I'll go. Deal?" He says, as he looks at me.

I smirk and say, "Deal." Omg me and X are making future plans, is this real? Am I finally getting what I always wanted from him? The next day it's Monday morning and it seems like things are finally at peace. I walk into my math class and sit down with the biggest appreciation for my life. X and I are in love, and there's no Britney getting in the way. My mom kicked James out and she's going to start an AA program. Before school started, Ashley told me about how her date with Kevin was amazing, and how happy she is that she went for it. He took her out to eat to at a nice restaurant and then they had sex for hours. It sounded ideal for her. Apparently, Kevin and Matt made up, and hugged it out like brothers. Matt told Kevin he's going to try coming out to his parents soon. I couldn't believe it, but I'm happy for him.

I walk into class and take a seat. I'm always early for this class. I feel a tap on my shoulder.

"Hey, did you do the homework?" I hear from the girl behind me. I turn around and say, "yeah I did, wanna copy it? You have to be quick before the teacher comes." Then I pass the girl my homework and she copies it way too fast. "Thank you so much, I owe you! What's your name?" She asks. "My name is Glend, I think we went to middle school together, you look really familiar." I say. She looks confused.

"Probably, well thank you again. My name is Annie, I'll hit you up if I ever need more homework. Don't sit too far please, I need someone like you around." I let out a huge smile.

"Annie? That's a pretty name, well if you need me here, I'll be here." I turn around and wait for class to begin. This is what normal feels like.

Life is as sweet as can be. The world is bright and I'm happy. I want to maintain this happiness for as long as I can. Things are finally going the way I want it to. I look at the clock and realize the teacher sure is taking a while. I feel my phone vibrate and wonder if it's X. I check quickly and it's from a number I don't recognize. The message says, "Glend?" I text back "Yes? Who's this?" A few seconds later, they respond saying, "Don't worry about who this is. You're going to find out soon. I know your secret, and if you don't do exactly what I say, I'm going to expose your little boyfriend." WHAT THE FUCK? This can't be for real. I start looking around the class to see if anyone is watching me.

I respond saying, "I don't know what you're talking about. I don't have a boyfriend." 30 seconds pass and I get another message with an attachment. "Don't play dumb. Isn't this you two kissing in front of his house?" When I open the attachment, it's a picture of X and I kissing in his car in front of his house. My entire body goes numb. What kind of sick game is this? I start panicking but I can't make it obvious since I'm in class. I'm about to start hyperventilating.I get one last message saying, "I'm pretty sure you're scared. I would be too. Your little boyfriend is about to get outed if you don't do exactly what I say. I'll text you soon. Until then, don't do anything stupid,

because I'll post this picture and many more on every Social Media platform. Have a great day!"
The teacher finally walks in and greets the class. "Sorry guys, I had to get something at the principal's office." She looks around and then looks directly at me.
"Jesus Glend, loosen up a bit. You look like you just saw someone get killed." The whole class starts laughing. I'm completely frozen. Everything is moving in slow motion. I can't move. All I can do is blink. What should I do? Do I tell someone? Do I keep this to myself? I feel my phone vibrate again and my body naturally reacts. It's a message from X. "I miss you so much. Thank you for being patient with me. This new beginning is going to work, I know it. I love you. Can't wait to see you after school."

Welp, now what? X is just coming around to the idea of being out with me, if he gets outed like this, it could really hurt him. Why would someone do this to him? Why would they do this to us? What did we ever do to them? "The only one who knew how to solve this equation was Glend, everyone, give him a round of applause." The teacher says. The class begins clapping.
"Well Glend, one thing about you, you'll always find X.. Ok class, everyone turn to page 291 for…." Her voice starts fading out. Find X? I'm about to lose mine. Oh no. What the fuck do I do?

Printed in the USA
CPSIA information can be obtained
at www.ICGtesting.com
LVHW052029130823
754932LV00008B/1104

9 798987 388518